THE THERMODYNAMICS
OF ELECTRICAL
PHENOMENA IN METALS

THE MACMILLAN COMPANY
NEW YORK · BOSTON · CHICAGO · DALLAS
ATLANTA · SAN FRANCISCO

MACMILLAN & CO., Limited
LONDON · BOMBAY · CALCUTTA
MELBOURNE

**THE MACMILLAN COMPANY
OF CANADA, Limited**
TORONTO

HE THERMODYNAMICS OF ELECTRICAL PHENOMENA IN METALS

BY

P. W. BRIDGMAN

NEW YORK
THE MACMILLAN COMPANY
1934

PREFACE

The following pages contain essentially the substance of a number of papers which I have written during the last ten years on inter-relations of a thermodynamic character between various electrical properties of metals. These papers are given in detail in the list of references at the end of the book.

The substance of these papers has been here consolidated into a more or less coherent whole, some extensions and new relations have been added, a couple of suggestions made as to new experimental possibilities, and several important modifications or corrections made in some of the original formulas. My original treatment of photo-electric phenomena has to be modified to meet our new apprehension of the experimental situation, emphasized by Fowler, that the photo-electric threshold is not sharp at ordinary temperatures but under stimulation of a single frequency electrons of a *range* of velocities are emitted. This modification probably does not mean any great qualitative change in many of the relations which I previously deduced, but the deduction becomes more complicated, the relations are less clean cut, and the situation cannot be finally clarified until much more and better experimental material is available. A suggestion which I made about cold electron emission under intense fields turns out on further analysis not to be pertinent, but to be concerned with another and simpler phenomenon, not of particular importance experimentally; this is treated briefly in Chapter V. One of the relations which I had previously deduced between the four transverse galvanomagnetic effects turns out to be erroneous; this clarifies the situation because previously there were too many relations to allow consistency with experiment. The final chapter on miscellanies contains much material not in my original papers, but more or less common property, and added for completeness.

No attempt whatever has been made to refer to all the work of others, or to make this treatment in any sense exhaustive. The discussion is, however, carried back sufficiently to its elements so that it should be self-contained and possible to read without reference to other works except for a background of the most rudimentary information. I would lay particular emphasis on the discussion of fundamental matters in the Introduction and Chapter I, because I feel that an adequate conception of fundamentals in this field is not common, and that the attitude of physicists toward these fundamentals cannot help but react on all attempts to understand the electrical properties of metals.

CONTENTS

INTRODUCTION

The progress of physics is unsystematic. The activities of the moment are determined by the most compelling interests of physicists at that moment, and into this enter many complex and human elements. There is a little of the element of sheer fashion, for most physicists are gregarious and enjoy talking over common activities with their fellows; there is the strategical element, for it is only human prudence to cultivate the fields in which success is most probable, and this usually means a new field; and there is the economic element, which demands that an experiment shall not involve too costly an apparatus. The development of physics is thus not always in that direction which would be taken by a competent dictator, charged with the task of getting intellectual mastery of the physical world as rapidly as possible, nor, indeed, is it in the direction which would be chosen by the majority of physicists themselves, if they could be freed from ulterior considerations. The result is that physics sometimes passes on to new territory before sufficiently consolidating territory already entered; it assumes sometimes too easily that results are secure and bases further advance on them, thereby laying itself open to future possible retreat. This is easy to understand in a subject in which development of the great fundamental concepts is often slow; a new generation appears before the concept has been really salted down, and assumes in the uncritical enthusiasm of youth that everything taught it in school is gospel truth, and forgets the doubts and tentative gropings of the great founders in its eagerness to make applications of the concepts and pass on to the next triumph.

In particular has all this been true of the development of our theories of the electrical properties of matter. The historical development of the fundamental ideas spread over a long time, sixty years from Poisson to the formulation of the field equations

1

for stationary bodies by Maxwell, to pick out two important landmarks. It is true that the expression for the mechanical action of an electric current was formulated at once by Ampère in its final form "leaping, full grown and full armed, from the brain of the 'Newton of electricity,'" to quote Maxwell, but this was only an episode and a rare exception. The ideas of the proper way to measure the strength of an electric current, the equivalence of static and current electricity, the conception of resistance and the proper way of measuring it, the conception of electromotive force, all were of slow growth, and involved continual rumination and chewing of the cud of contemplation to determine whether the picture that was forming itself was a consistent picture and capable of including new facts as they were discovered. But each new young physicist, as he enters the lists, is in danger of forgetting all the past rumination and the present uncertainty, and of starting with an uncritical acceptance of the concepts in the stage of development in which he finds them.

The electrical concepts entered a stage of crystallization with the formulation of the field equations by Maxwell. The experience back of the equations was a pretty exhaustive knowledge of electrical phenomena in empty space (except for radio phenomena), but with regard to the electrical properties of material bodies the range of experimental material was much more restricted, and was confined to comparatively simple conditions, such as isotropic bodies at constant temperature. The electrical properties of matter are, however, most complicated, and many of them have been discovered since the crystallization of the concepts. Some of these are included in the phenomena with which we shall be specially concerned here: thermo-electric properties, including Peltier and Thomson thermal effects, the Volta effect, thermionic emission, photo-electric emission, auto-electric emission (cold discharges in intense fields), phenomena in crystals, including anisotropic resistance and various reversible heating effects, and various effects in the magnetic field, of which the Hall effect is the best known. Each of these effects, as discovered, should have been carefully scrutinized, to find whether it fitted into the scheme already evolved, or whether modification was demanded. Such an examination, because it is nobody's business, and because the fundamental concepts have already been accepted, is in danger of being made superficially, without the care that would have been given it if the effect had been known at the time the concept was formulated. To take a simple example: how many physicists have ever seen the field equations of Maxwell written out for the interior of a conductor carrying a current in a magnetic field in which there is a Hall effect, or indeed how many physicists could tell whether field equations are possible in a medium exhibiting the Hall effect? Yet every conducting medium carrying a current is a seat of a magnetic field and therefore of a Hall effect, and the Hall coefficient should enter somewhere into the field equations, even although the effect may be numerically unimportant.

Historically, the development of new points of view and the discovery of new experimental facts came too rapidly for complete assimilation into what was already known. A further difficulty, of course, is that the experimental facts are often not discovered in the logical order. The electron theory came crowding on the heels of the formulation of the field equations, with its thesis that the properties of all matter could be explained in terms of the motion of concealed discrete electrical particles, and that the motion of these particles was controlled by the field equations, extrapolated to miscroscopic dimensions hopelessly beyond direct experimental verification, and before their validity had been checked even over the entire experimental domain. And finally, crowding on the heels of electron theory, is wave mechanics, forced on us by the new experimental facts of atomic physics, in which we give up the idea of discrete electrical particles with individuality, but retain the concept of the electrodynamic field to control the motion of what replaces the electron, and determine the magnitude of this field (as, for example, in the neighborhood of the nucleus of an atom) in terms of a fictitious discrete elementary charge acting after the fashion of the charges of large scale experience.

In the face of a historical development like this it would not be surprising if points had been missed, and it seems to be worth while that at least one physicist should attempt a critical review and record somewhere his findings. It seems to me that two important sorts of thing have been missed. In the first place, there are relations between the various effects which are demanded by the broad general principles of thermodynamics. Apart from the intrinsic interest in these relations, many of which are new, they are of importance in directing the development of any detailed theory because it is necessary, on the one hand, that the theory be capable of giving an account of these relations, but, on the other hand, the fact that the theory can give an account of the relation raises no presumption whatever as to the truth of the theory. The establishment of such a result by any theory is merely a check on its correct formal working out, since any theory, not violating the most general principles, must be consistent with thermodynamics. It is important to know *all* the thermodynamic relations, in order that no theory may derive a spurious support from its ability to deduce a relation of this sort. The second sort of thing which I believe to have been missed is the fact that the concepts themselves, in terms of which we have attempted to describe the electrical state inside a metal, are not broad enough, but have to be amplified in a way which turns out not to be difficult.

Insistence on the importance of the general relations of thermodynamics does not obscure our recognition that eventually nothing will satisfy the physicist except a detailed picture which will make possible not only an explicit derivation of all the relations obtainable from general considerations, but also a derivation of all the other special relations.

CHAPTER I

EXAMINATION OF FUNDAMENTALS

We start with an examination of the fundamental notions and experiments involved in the notion of the electrical field, and, following convention, we shall first be concerned with electrostatics. The experiments discussed in the following are largely idealized experiments introduced to show the nature of the fundamental ideas; we shall not be concerned with questions of experimental accuracy or feasibility.

Consider first experiments made in empty space with bodies all of whose dimensions are of microscopic size and which carry electrical charges. By measuring the force acting between various pairs of these charged bodies at different distances we arrive at the ideas of quantity of electricity and the inverse square law of force. By studying the force under the mutual action of several bodies we find that the force is additive. In terms of the force exerted on a single one of these bodies carrying a unit charge at various distances from a system composed of others of our charged bodies held in a rigid framework we develop the idea of a field of force at every point of space, equal to the force on unit charge, and the idea of the potential of this field. Mathematically we find that the force field surrounding a distribution of charges acting according to the inverse square law is a conservative field. We find mathematically that the total charge inside a closed region is determined by an integral of the force over a surface enclosing that region.

We next allow some of our charged bodies to become of finite size, and make the discovery that the force at a fixed point of space experienced by a charged test body of microscopic dimensions carrying unit charge is not equal to twice the force experienced by another microscopic body carrying a double charge.

More generally, the force experienced by a test charge in the presence of two charged metallic bodies of finite size is not the sum of the forces experienced first with only one charged body present and then with the other. But we discover that as we make the charge on our test body smaller, the limit of the ratio of force to charge approaches a definite limit, which we now define as the electric field at a point in the field due to charged bodies of finite size.* This is evidently consistent with the previous definition of the field in the presence of charged bodies all of microscopic dimensions, and we therefore now redefine the field at a point as in all cases equal to the limit of the ratio of force to charge. Our previous mathematical theorems continue to apply : the field has a potential and is conservative and Gauss's theorem holds.

In spite of the fact that a charged metallic body of finite size is not surrounded by a constant force field rigidly attached to it, we find by applying Gauss's theorem to a surface surrounding the charged metal that as long as the metal remains isolated from its surroundings the total charge which it bears remains constant no matter what other charged bodies are present. We discover that if two charged metals of finite size which bear numerically equal but opposite charges are brought into contact, so as to become effectively a single body, the system becomes electrically neutral, the field vanishing at every point. This condition of affairs would be exactly brought about by a proper rearrangement in the bodies of their original charges, which together totaled zero. We are thereby led to the conception of electrical conductors in which charges may move about, and we seek to explain, by the displacements of the electrical charge in the conductor, the failure of a single charged conductor to surround itself with a rigidly attached field.

A detailed examination of the field surrounding charged conductors shows that as we approach the surface of such a conduc-

---

* It is of course not possible in any actual experiment to let the test charge really approach zero ; the justification for our definition is that as a matter of experiment the ratio of force to charge remains sensibly constant after the charge has decreased below a certain size, and we assume that there would be no further departures from this constant value if at some time in the future we were able to make experiments with very much smaller charges than those which we can now handle.

tor the field always becomes normal to the surface, the component along the surface vanishing. Examination of the fields about many conductors leads finally to this generalized picture : the total charge on each conductor remains constant in amount, but rearranges itself in such a way that the surface of the conductor is always an equipotential surface ; the interior of the conductor is a region free from a field, and the charge resides entirely on the surface.

In arriving at this picture we have made several steps that require careful examination. In saying that the interior of the conductor is free from field we have passed beyond quantities with direct physical meaning and have introduced mathematical constructions. The field in empty space was defined in terms of physical measurements that were capable of approximate execution, for although of course the test charge could not actually be made to go to zero, we could at least approach to the idealized definition by actual physical measurements. But no such measurements of force can be executed, even ideally, in the interior of a metallic conductor, and the field inside a conductor therefore becomes a construction, so designed as to degenerate under the proper conditions into the constructions already made. In particular, the field at internal points of the conductor is calculated by the inverse square law from the position of all electrical charges, exactly as in the simple original case where we had only microscopic bodies in empty space, disregarding the fact that part of space may now be filled with conducting bodies. In other words, the conductor is not supposed to exert any effect on the propagation of force from one point to another ; unit charge at the center of a heavy metallic spherical shell produces in our calculations exactly the same field at external points as if the shell were not present. With this convention about the meaning to be assigned to "field" in regions where the physical measurements cannot be executed, it is found, as already suggested, that the measurable fields at external points can always be calculated by assuming that the total charge on conductors collects on the surface in such a way as to leave the interior free from field.

The idea that the interior of a metal must be free from field appeals to us very much, because it fits into a picture consistent with our previous experience. A metal is pictured as the seat of positive and negative charges, normally present in equal amounts, and mingled together, so as to be neutral electrically, but freely moveable and separable under the action of any force. The interior of a conductor in a static condition, according to this picture, cannot be a region in which there is a net force acting on electricity, for this would produce a continual motion of the electricity in the metal and so lead to a non-static condition. Now assuming that in the interior of the metal there are no forces not derivable from the inverse square law acting on the electricity, and also picturing the force which the electric field exerts on the distributed electricity as determined by the product of charge and field in exactly the same way as the force on one of our original test bodies of microscopic dimensions, we are led at once to the conclusion that our constructional field must vanish inside the metal. Gauss's theorem demands that there can be no net charge in a region free from force, so that the interior of the conductor must be free from charge as well as force, and the charge must all reside on the surface. But at the surface of the conductor we must assume forces which restrain the charge from leaving the surface, since it is an easy matter to prove that the total forces derived from the inverse square law exert a resultant, $2\pi\rho^2$, on the surface charge perpendicular to the surface, where ρ is "surface density" of charge. The forces which prevent the charge from leaving the surface under this so-called "boiler pressure" force must be described as non-electrical forces. This non-electrical force is exactly equal and opposite to the electrical force, and has no component tangential to the surface, since the electrical force has no tangential component.

The picture thus obtained is very simple and pleasing, but from the mathematical point of view it is not uniquely determined by the conditions in the region of physical meaning of the solution. For example, we would obtain exactly the same field at external points if we supposed the neighborhood of the surface of the conductor to be a double layer arrangement, the region between the layers being by hypothesis incapable of physical exploration, so constructed that one half the net charge is always constrained to remain in the outer layer and one half in the inner layer, each layer itself being an equipotential surface. An infinite number of other solutions are also possible in which some of the charge resides in the interior of the metal. The reason that we adopt a mathematical construction which is not uniquely demanded by the physical measurements is, in the first place, because it is the simplest, and in the second place because it fits in most consistently with other physical experience which we have not yet brought explicitly into the picture. We have no evidence from other sorts of phenomena of inhomogeneities inside the metal, and we would be merely going out of our way to adopt a picture for electrical phenomena which demanded such inhomogeneities merely because they were not forbidden by the mathematics. The mathematical construction actually adopted furthermore has the very pleasing property that, subject to the additional assumptions about homogeneity, etc., it is uniquely determined everywhere, not only where measurements may be made, but within the body of the metal. The quality of uniqueness is intimately associated, in the minds of most of us, with the idea of "reality," so that we may think of the solution which we have adopted as having "physical reality."

The introduction of mathematical constructions in regions where in the very nature of things no direct corresponding physical operation can be carried out must not be thought to be by any means reprehensible, but is something to which we are continually forced in all our physical theorizing. This is shown by the very simplest sorts of example; for instance, our idea that the interiors of the bodies which surround us are uniformly occupied by homogeneous material can never be directly verified, because our exploration of the interior itself destroys the homogeneity which we are seeking to establish. The picture of a homogeneous interior is a construction, so simple and useful as to be almost inevitable, and unconsciously endowed with complete "reality." A somewhat more complicated sort of thing is the stress inside a solid body. We never directly measure a stress; this is a complicated mathematical construction describing the condition at inaccessible interior points, and connected in a definite way with the forces acting across the surface of the body, which can be measured directly. The usefulness of such constructions is in large measure determined by the correlations which they make possible with physical phenomena not in the original picture; as, for example, the optical double refraction observed in a transparent body across whose surface forces are acting may be predicted in terms of the stresses. There is nothing inherently objectionable, therefore, in the concept of a field at inaccessible points inside solid bodies, but we must demand that this construction fit consistently with other constructions that we may be forced to make, and with other physical information not contained in the original picture.

Our physical experiments with charged conductors have compelled another pregnant extension of our original ideas, namely, the introduction of the idea of a surface density of electricity on the surface of the conductor to describe the state of the electricity in the surface. We started with systems composed of charged bodies of microscopic dimensions; we later introduced test charges to determine the field, but always our electrical system could be regarded as built up of electrical particles. The force on electricity is given in terms of the particle picture, the product of field strength and charge, the charge having only magnitude and no other structure. But on the surface of a conductor our mathematics demands a continuous distribution. Later, in dealing with phenomena in dielectrics, which we shall not discuss here, we find it desirable to still further generalize this picture, and think of continuous distributions of electricity in three dimensions. Now a uniformly distributed medium is a more complicated thing than a particle, and one would at once expect new parameters to be necessary in order to describe it completely. For example, one would expect the analog of the stresses of ordinary solids and gases, and these stresses would be expected to enter the equations of equilibrium along with the forces arising from the field. But the possible existence of stresses in addition to volume forces, to which we are thus led, is merely ignored in the conventional development of the subject and the implications in such possibilities are not at all examined. It is recognized that if a conductor bears a surface charge of density ρ, the field exerts on this charge a total force directed normally away from the conductor of $2\pi\rho^2$ per unit area. It is recognized that in some way the material of the conductor must exert on the surface charge an equal and opposite total normal force of $2\pi\rho^2$, but no attempt is made to analyze this action further, and in fact the significance of the mere fact that we are thus compelled to recognize the existence of forces acting on electricity which cannot be derived from the field is usually lost sight of. Moreover, whenever it proves convenient to picture the electrical state of the interior of a massive body in terms of a volume distribution of electricity we go even further than in treating surface charges, and set the total force acting on electricity as the product of field strength and charge density, ignoring not only a possible effect arising from the hypothetical analog with internal stresses in the electrical medium, but completely forgetting the possibility of non-electrical forces which we know must exist in the case of surface charges. Fortunately in the simple case of a homogeneous metallic conductor at constant temperature carrying no current (or even carrying a steady current, as appears later) these complications can have no effect, because the volume density of electric charge is zero under such conditions, and there is therefore no room for such effects. But if more complicated cases should arise, in which perhaps the conductor becomes non-homogeneous, thus making possible the existence of distributed charges within it, or cases in which it is necessary to scrutinize the transfer of electricity from one conductor to another across surfaces which need not be simple, we may be on the lookout for difficulties arising from the neglect of these effects.

Passing on now to more complicated conditions, we give up the requirement that the system be in a steady state, and study simple systems in which there are linear currents. We may best approach this subject from the standpoint of static electricity. Given two large metallic conductors of the same metal, charged with equal and opposite amounts of electricity, connected by a long and very fine wire of the *same metal*. It is found that the electric field in the space surrounding the conductors does not remain steady, but gradually drops toward zero, which it eventually reaches at every point of space and the system becomes electrically neutral. This phenomenon, consistently with our previous experience with conductors, is naturally ascribed to the passage of charge through the wire from one conductor to the other, this passage thus constituting an electric current. The magnitude of the current is simply defined in terms of the rate at which the conductors are losing charge, and this may be determined by an application of Green's theorem to surfaces surrounding each of the conductors. It can furthermore be established by direct exploration of the field surrounding the conductors that the rate at which the current is flowing in the wire is proportional to the instantaneous difference of potential between the conductors, as measured by an exploring charge of infinitesimal size moved through intervening empty space from a point immediately outside one conductor to a point immediately outside the other. The constant of proportionality between current and difference of potential between the conductors is found to be simply connected with the properties of the connecting wire, being inversely as its length and directly as its cross section. The constant also changes when the metal of which the system is constructed is changed. The concept thus arises of a resistance to current flow offered by the metal of the wire, and a new constant of the metal is recognized, its specific resistance. Because of the inverse dependence of total resistance on cross section, the current in the wire is pictured as uniformly distributed over its entire cross section. Here again we are dealing with a construction, for the distribution of current in the solid conductor cannot be directly examined. It is, however, almost an inevitable construction, as shown by experiments on compound conductors built up of many fine wires. A simple picture thus develops of the condition at interior points of a conductor in which a steady current is flowing. The current flows because the conductor is the seat of an electric field acting on the electricity which is always present in the body of the conductor; the intensity of the current is directly as this field, and inversely as the resistance. If the current is steady, this demands that the divergence of the field at interior points vanish, and this by Gauss's theorem means that there can be no internal charge density. We have the paradox of electricity in motion through a region in which there is no electricity. The paradox is resolved by recognizing that only one of the two kinds of electricity originally present in equal quantities in the metal need be in motion, the other remaining stationary. A mathematical indetermination now appears, however, because a motion of positive electricity in one direction is as effective as motion of negative electricity in the other direction, or indeed all intermediate states of combined motion are possible. The origin of the field in the conducting wire is found in a distribution of charge over the surface of the wire, as revealed by an exploration of the electric field outside the wire. Mathematically, the requirements that there be a constant field inside, that any charges be located entirely on the surface of the conductor, and that the field everywhere shall be determined from the charges by the inverse square law, are found always to lead to a possible solution, which furthermore is unique. The solution at interior points of the wire, which is only a mathematical construction, thus acquires the status of physical reality. Notice again that under these simple conditions we say that the force on the electricity inside the wire is determined only by the electric field; our scruples as to possible non-electric forces or actions analogous to stresses are laid by the observation that the electric charge density vanishes, so that other actions would not be expected to exist. It is not so obvious, however, what to expect in more complicated cases.

Experiment also discloses in the neighborhood of a wire carrying a current a magnetic field. This can be simply calculated from the distribution of the current; the details are not of interest here. The important point is that by measuring the magnetic field we have an independent method of measuring the current, so that we may give physical meaning to the current in those cases in which it is not possible, as above, to determine the current in terms of an actual transfer of charge from one place to another. There are other phenomena accompanying a current, such as chemical effects, which may also be used to give independent meaning to current strength, although perhaps not as simply as the magnetic effects.

Among the phenomena accompanying flow of current there is a heating effect in the wire. The rate at which heat is generated is precisely equal to the rate at which the electrostatic energy of the charged conductors at the ends of the wire is disappearing, the energy being determined in terms of the charges and their potentials. The total generation of heat between the initial fully charged state and the final state of complete neutrality is the initial total electrostatic energy of the distribution. The rate at which heat is generated in the body of the conductor is i^2r per unit volume. Since the electric field $\mathcal{E}$ is equal to ir, the rate of heat generation might also be written as $i\mathcal{E}$. $\mathcal{E}$ is the difference of potential of points unit distance apart, and i is the quantity of electricity per unit time. The heat may then be rewritten as $q\Delta V$, which is the work done when quantity q of electricity flows between two points at potential difference ΔV. Under these conditions the work received is entirely turned into heat. The details of the conversion of the original electrostatic energy of the distribution into heat may be followed by means of the Poynting vector. This vector is $\dfrac{1}{4\pi}\,\mathcal{E}\times H$. It may be determined at any point by independent measurements of electric and magnetic fields, and is a possible expression for the energy crossing unit area in unit time. The excess of influx over efflux into a given region in unit time of the Poynting vector (that is, its divergence) represents energy deposited in the region, which must therefore appear in some recognizable form. It is found that the net Poynting vector influx into the wire connecting our two charged conductors exactly accounts for the energy appearing as heat. The other ends of the lines of the Poynting vector are distributed through the space where there is an electric field. The picture is one of transfer into the wire along the Poynting vector of the electrostatic energy originally distributed throughout the electric field in empty space; in the wire this energy appears as heat.

The conversion of electrostatic energy into heat is completely irreversible, like any friction effect; it is not possible by uniformly raising the temperature of a conductor to produce a current of electricity in it.

Although for formal purposes it is possible to develop our notions of electric currents from the discharge of quasi-electrostatic systems, there is one important difference between such currents and the currents which we usually encounter. The current from the quasi-static system slowly decays until the system becomes electrically neutral, whereas most of the currents of practice may continue to flow at their original strength indefinitely. For example, the current from a battery flows indefinitely as long as we renew the chemicals of the battery. Such systems evidently contain some source of action fundamentally different from that in the static system. As far as the wire is concerned, in which the current flows when connected to the terminals of the battery, there is no reason to think that the action is any different from that when the same wire is used to discharge a condenser. Detailed exploration of the field surrounding the wire bears out this expectation; if the current in the wire is so adjusted as to be the same in the two cases, as determined for example by its magnetic field, the electric field in the surrounding space is also the same. This electric field at the surface of the wire has both normal and tangential components, the tangential component indicating a field inside the wire which drives the current. This tangential component has its origin in a surface charge distributed along the wire with *varying* density, the actual density at any point being determined by the normal component of the field. Inside of the wire, therefore, we must think of the current as maintained by an electric field derived by the inverse square law from suitably situated electric charges. These charges are maintained in position against the natural tendency of every electrical system on conductors to sink back to a position of electrical neutrality by the action of the battery. The battery is the seat of some sort of action by which a difference of electric potential is maintained between its terminals. This difference of potential may be directly measured if the battery is open circuited by exploring with a test charge the space between terminals attached to the electrodes of the battery, taking the precaution to make the terminals of the same metal. This is also the difference of potential found by an exploration between the ends of a wire joining the terminals in which a steady current is flowing, provided that the wire is fine enough and the cross section of the battery sufficiently large. We may therefore measure the action of the battery by the difference of electrostatic potential which it is able to produce; we call this the electromotive force (E.M.F.) of the battery, and for simplicity put it equal to the potential difference. The current in the wire we already know to be equal to the difference of potential between its ends divided by its resistance, or $\Delta V/R$. If R is high enough, $\Delta V =$ E.M.F., and $i =$ E.M.F.$/R$. If the resistance of the wire is low, the current is less than would be given by this relation, but we find that for all values of R the current is given by $i =$ E.M.F.$/(R + r_b)$, and the inevitable interpretation is that r_b is to be ascribed to the internal resistance of the battery, a point of view which is checked by studying the effect of varying the cross section of the battery or the distance between the plates. In the external circuit, where the only action in the wire is an electric field derived by the inverse square law from charges, the current is $i = \Delta V/R$. In the whole circuit, in which there can be no net change of potential, since V derived from the inverse square law is conservative, the current is given by $i =$ E.M.F.$/(R + r_b)$. In the battery itself, because of the conservative property of the field, the inverse square potential must experience a rise equal to its drop in the rest of the circuit; in spite of this rise current flows in the battery in the same direction as in the rest of the circuit. The obvious reason is that the E.M.F. in the battery overcomes the backward drive of the electric field, producing a net force in the forward direction. In fact, we find at once, for the inside of the battery $i = ($E.M.F. $ - \Delta V)/r_b$, the ΔV having the same value as already demanded, namely

$$\Delta V = \frac{R}{R + r_b}\,\text{E.M.F.}$$

The energy manifestations in the wire connecting the terminals of the battery are thus the same as those in the same wire in which the same current flows when discharging a condenser. There is a uniform generation of heat in the wire, the total heat per unit time being $i^2 R = i\Delta V$. The energy gets into the wire on the Poynting vector, which at the wire has exactly the same configuration as in the case of the condenser. Detailed tracing out of the Poynting vector shows, however, that the other end of the vector does not originate at points in space where electric energy of the field is situated, but the origin of the Poynting flux is in the battery, the total efflux from the battery being exactly equal to the total influx into the wire. The source of the thermal energy appearing in the wire is therefore the battery, as indeed it must be, because there is no other possibility. This conclusion may be checked by studying the chemical transformations which take place in the battery when current flows. The total heat supplied by the battery to the external circuit is therefore $i^2R = i\Delta V = i\dfrac{R}{R + r_b}$ (E.M.F.). By analogy we expect an internal heating in the battery because of the current flowing through its internal resistance. This we put $= i^2 r_b = i(\text{E.M.F.} - \Delta V) = i\dfrac{r_b}{R + r_b}$ (E.M.F.). The total heat is the sum of these or $i \times$ E.M.F., which is the total rate at which energy is supplied by the E.M.F. of the battery as current flows through it.

In the case of the battery the relations are, therefore, exceedingly simple. $i = (\text{E.M.F.} - \Delta V)/r_b$, Ohm's law, and rate of work of battery $= i \times$ E.M.F., where ΔV is the difference of electrostatic potential in going through the battery *between terminals of the same metal* and E.M.F. measures the action of the battery. It is to be noticed that the E.M.F. may be obtained either from a measurement of the total heating effect by means of the energy equation, or it may be obtained from a measurement of the current from the expression for Ohm's law. It is also to be noticed that we have not had to go inside the battery in any of this analysis; the quantities entering our equations are all derived from measurements actually made in the space outside the battery. We are therefore dealing with actual physical quantities, not constructions, and our results may be checked by direct measurement.

We now seek to generalize what we have obtained, and in particular ask what is the potential within the battery itself. We first simplify to the extreme by supposing that the action in the battery takes place uniformly in the space between its electrodes. If the distance between electrodes is l, then the average of the total E.M.F. taken per unit of length is E.M.F./l, which we write as e.m.f. The average of ΔV per unit length is $\Delta V/l = - \mathcal{E}$, where $\mathcal{E}$ is the electric vector. If we take the cross section of the battery as unity, write r for the specific resistance of the material of the battery, and write the equations above for unit length of the battery, we obviously have for the current density

$$i = \frac{(\text{e.m.f.} + \mathcal{E})}{r} \qquad \text{I, 1,}$$

and for the rate at which the battery supplies energy per unit volume

$$i \times \text{e.m.f.} \qquad \text{I, 2.}$$

These local values obviously give correct results when integrated over the complete circuit, because they were so constructed.

The conventional and classical development of the subject now assumes that these results hold universally, and may be applied in the most general case where we have to recognize that the source of the action which is capable of maintaining a current is distributed continuously throughout a volume. In the application of these equations it is supposed to make no difference whether or not the material is homogeneous, or whether it is at uniform temperature, or whether there is a volume distribution of charge in the region of action.

In the two equations all the quantities are directly measurable except the e.m.f. In I, 2 the energy supplied by the source of the e.m.f. in unit volume is directly measurable by a study of the changes taking place in unit volume, chemical changes if the source of energy is chemical, or thermal input if the source is thermal as in a thermo-couple, or other changes for other sorts of action. The i of this equation may be obtained from measurements of the surrounding magnetic field. In I, 1 occurs the same i. The r of this equation may be obtained from the irreversible Joulean heat with different currents, and the $\mathcal{E}$ of this equation may in principle be determined by locating the electric charges by exploration with a test charge, and then integrating by the inverse square law of force.* The thesis involved in writing

---

* I do not want to complicate the discussion by considering in detail what happens when the system contains parts in motion, as in a dynamo. It will be sufficient to say that in such more general cases the $\mathcal{E}$ is the $\mathcal{E}$ which satisfies the Maxwell equations, and it may be determined in terms of the charges and certain boundary conditions at surfaces of discontinuity in the motion, where there is located a "surface curl" of $\mathcal{E}$. In such systems containing moving parts $\mathcal{E}$ is not derivable from a scalar potential, and it is not conservative, but nevertheless $\mathcal{E}$ may be given a meaning at every point of the system.

these two equations for the most general case now is that the e.m.f. found by solving the first after substituting into it the measurable quantities will be the same as the e.m.f. found by similarly solving the second. But we have already seen that in regions of inhomogeneity, where there may be distributed charges, complicated effects may be anticipated, perhaps analogous to those found in ordinary media in which a stress is acting. We might therefore anticipate that the two equations obtained from a generalization of very simple conditions might prove not to be adequate. This in fact I believe to be the case, and I shall later show that at least in the case of a metal carrying currents derived from a thermal electromotive force the action must be more complicated, and the e.m.f. derived from the first equation is not the same as that derived from the second.

We shall for the present satisfy ourselves with defining an e.m.f. which is obtained by the solution of equation 2 as a "working e.m.f." or $(e.m.f.)_w$, and one obtained from the solution of equation 1 as a "driving e.m.f." or $(e.m.f.)_d$. We thus have in general the equations:

Rate at which source delivers energy
$$= i \times (e.m.f.)_w \qquad\qquad \text{I, 3.}$$
$$i = \frac{(e.m.f.)_d + \mathcal{E}}{r} = \frac{(e.m.f.)_d - \text{Grad Pot}}{r} \qquad \text{I, 4.}$$

We now at last are ready to let drop the requirement that the various metallic bodies in our system are all of the same metal. Consider two metallic spheres of different metals, A and B, each being itself electrically neutral, as shown by the absence of any electric field in the surrounding space when explored by a small test charge. Now connect the two spheres by a fine wire, half

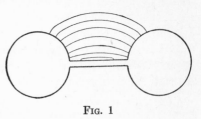

Fig. 1

of metal A and half of B. The exploring charge now reveals the presence of a static field in the surrounding space, lines of force running across from one sphere to the other, and also from one point of the connecting wire to another, as shown by Figure 1.

The configuration of the lines of force is such as to indicate one constant potential at all points immediately outside the metal A, whether this metal is found in the sphere or the wire, and another constant potential at all points outside the metal B. This is general; two different metals in contact apparently get themselves into such an electrical condition that there is a constant difference of potential between all points immediately outside one metal as compared with all points outside the other, the surface of each metal by itself remaining an equipotential surface, as we have already found in our experiments on systems of conductors all made of the same metal. We denote this difference of potential, which is called the Volta difference, by V_{AB}, indicating by the order of the letters the increase of potential on passing from a point outside A to one outside B, or $V_{AB} = V_B - V_A$. Application of Gauss's theorem to a small pill-box-shaped region, partly inside and partly outside the surface of the metal, as indicated in the figure, now demands at once that there be a surface charge on the conductor, if we assume as before that the interior of the conductor is a region free from field. It is almost necessary that we continue to assume this, for we can see no reason why conditions inside a mass of metal should be altered by moving another mass of metal about in the vicinity. The reality of the existence of this surface charge may be shown by a condenser experiment. Two parallel plates of A and B confront each other at a distance l_0. The field in the space between them is found to be uniform, of amount $\mathcal{E}_0$, directed from A toward B, where $\mathcal{E}_0 l_0 = V_{AB}$. This is in accordance with the fundamental experimental fact that the system comes to such a state that there is a constant potential difference between all points outside one metal as compared with the other. Gauss's theorem demands that on the surface of A there be a positive charge of superficial density $\rho_0 = \dfrac{1}{4\pi}\mathcal{E}_0 = \dfrac{V_{AB}}{4\pi l_0}$, and an equal density of negative charge on the surface of B, the surface charges on the two metals thus together totaling zero. Now change the distance between the plates to l_1. The charge on A now changes to $\dfrac{1}{4\pi}\mathcal{E}_1 = \dfrac{V_{AB}}{4\pi l_1}$, and the charge on B to the equal negative value. The change of surface charge can be brought about only by electricity passing through the connecting wire; the motion of charge constitutes an electric current in the wire. This current may be measured by its magnetic effects. The total quantity of electricity conveyed by the current during the change of the distance between the condenser plates may be measured with a ballistic galvanometer, and is $\dfrac{V_{AB}}{4\,\pi}\left[\dfrac{1}{l_1} - \dfrac{1}{l_0}\right]$ per unit surface of the condenser. Measurement of the ballistic throw gives at once, therefore, a method of measuring the Volta potential difference. This is the method of Kelvin, and is naturally much more accurate than the result of attempting to directly measure the field in the intervening space with a test charge.

The values which are obtained for the Volta difference of potential between two metals under ordinary laboratory conditions prove to be highly erratic, and long experimenting was necessary before it could be accepted as conclusively proved that the effect is highly sensitive to fluctuations in the surface conditions, films of absorbed gas or other substances too minute to be detected by ordinary methods being sufficient to entirely change the Volta differences. It now appears, however, that characteristic reproducible values can be obtained for the Volta differences if the experiments are made with the best modern high vacuum technique, taking pains to entirely clean the surfaces of the metals from foreign contamination. In the following it will be assumed that the experiments are made under these conditions.

The "Volta Law of Tensions" is found to apply to the Volta potential difference between different metals. This law states that if A, B, and C are any three metals, then

$$V_{AB} + V_{BC} = V_{AC} \qquad\qquad \text{I, 5.}$$

Applied to a closed system of three metals as indicated in Figure 2 this means that the sum of the three jumps of potential outside the three surfaces of separation of the metals must add to zero. This, however, is a necessary consequence of the fact that a system composed only of metals like this can have no permanent source of energy in it, as would be the case if there were a battery, for example, but must come to a stationary condition, in which at most there can be an electrostatic field at external points. But now the electrostatic field is conservative, and the total change of potential in a closed path is zero. Such a closed path is indicated in the figure. But the parts of this path indicated

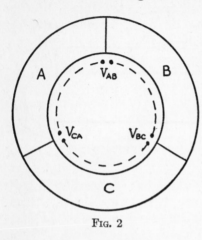

Fig. 2

by the dotted lines encounter no change of potential because of our fundamental experimental fact that the surface of a single metal not carrying a current comes to constant potential. The system, therefore, must automatically come to such a condition that the Volta law of tensions is satisfied, and it might appear that in enunciating the law we have not been saying much, but have committed a tautology. This, however, is not the case, but the significance of the Volta law is slightly different from what might be inferred from its customary formulation. The significance is not that the three potential differences add to zero, but that each of the three terms, V_{AB}, V_{BC}, and V_{AC} is characteristic of only that pair of metals appearing in the subscripts, and is always the same, independent of the presence in the system of other metals.

The Volta law of tensions may be formulated as:

$$V_{Ax} + V_{xB} = V_{AB}, \qquad \text{I, 6.}$$

where x is any metal, and V_{AB} does not depend on x. It is easy to show analytically that if this relation is satisfied it must be possible to split V_{Ax} into two parts, one of which depends only on A and the other in the same way on x, or in other words, we must have,

$$V_{Ax} = f(x) - f(A). \qquad \text{I, 7.}$$

That this is a sufficient condition is obvious at once on substituting back into the Volta law of tensions. That it is also necessary can be shown by a simple functional analysis which we need not bother with here. This resolution of V_{Ax} into two parts is not unique, but f is undetermined by a term the same for all metals, which may in general be a function of temperature. We shall find later a possible way of making this resolution.

Next consider various energy relations connected with the existence of a Volta effect. Imagine the two condenser plates of Figure 3 with the wire between them broken, and separately charged to equal and opposite surface densities, such that the difference of potential between points immediately outside them, as found by a test charge, is V. Connect them by a wire fine enough so that the plates slowly

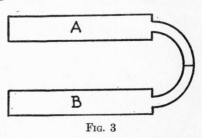

Fig. 3

discharge. The current in the wire may be measured by a galvanometer; the heating effect in the wire during the discharge may also be measured. The fundamental fact is now found that the total heating effect while the quantity of electricity q flows between the plates at potential difference V is not qV, as it was in the simple case of a condenser made of two plates of the same metal, but is now

$$q(V - V_{BA}).$$ I, 7 *bis.*

That is, the effective potential difference in the wire from which energy is derived by the passage of electricity must be figured from the threshold value V_{BA} to which the system automatically sinks back. But now the conditions in the wire itself, while heat is being generated by the motion of current against resistance, must be thought of as the same as when the system is all of the same metal. It would appear, then, as though in this compound system consisting of two metals the effective potentials *in* the metals were different from the potentials measured between points immediately outside the metals.

This at once gives a clue to the sort of action that may be responsible for the existence of the Volta effect. We apparently want some sort of discontinuity of the potential on passing across the surface into the metal. Mathematical analysis provides what is wanted in the fiction of a double surface layer. A plane parallel condenser charged to potential difference V receives a surface charge of density $\dfrac{1}{4\pi}\dfrac{V}{l}$, where l is the distance of separation of the plates. If now l is allowed to approach zero at the same time that the surface density increases in such a way that V remains constant, we are left in the limit with a surface of discontinuity of potential on which there is a distribution of doublets with axis perpendicular to the surface. The relations here are reversible : a discontinuity of potential demands a double layer and a double layer demands a discontinuity of potential. Imagine now a spherical conductor surrounded with such a double layer. Gauss's theorem shows that there is no field at either external or internal points ; the only effect of such a double layer is to raise the potential of the entire interior of the sphere by a uniform amount above that of the surroundings. As long as we stay outside the body of the metal there is no method by which the physical existence of such a double layer can be detected. The same state of affairs holds no matter what the shape of the conductor.

This jump in potential at the surface is entirely independent of the presence of any ordinary surface charges on the surface, for such charges produce no discontinuity of potential.

If now we suppose that on the surface of all metallic conductors there are double layers, we have the sort of thing required. If

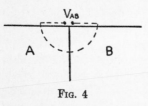

FIG. 4

in Figure 4 there are constant double layers and therefore constant jumps of potential at the three surfaces separating A from B, A from empty space, and B from empty space, then the existence of a constant Volta jump V_{AB} between points immediately outside A and B is at once provided for, as we see on describing the closed path indicated by the dotted line, and applying the condition that the total change of potential in any closed path must be zero, and also the condition that in the body of the massive metal there can be no potential gradient if the state of affairs is steady, as we assume. The relation between the jumps is obviously:

$$V_{AB} = \text{(Internal jump } A \text{ to } B\text{)} + \text{(Jump } B \text{ to empty space)} + \text{(Jump empty space to } A\text{)}$$
$$= V'_{AB} \qquad\qquad + V_{BE} \qquad\qquad - V_{AE}. \qquad \text{I, 8.}$$

The existence of a Volta potential jump is thus provided for, but the solution we have obtained is not determinate; we are obviously not able to assign unique values to the three quantities on the right-hand side of equation 8 on the basis of the single condition that their sum shall be fixed. It is important to emphasize, however, that the existence of the jump V_{AB} demands the existence of some other compensating jump, and therefore the existence of an electrostatic double layer somewhere on the surface (1) or (2) or (3), or in suitable combination on all three; we cannot get rid of a double layer somewhere.

Various hypotheses have been set up to partition exactly the potential jumps between the three possible surfaces, and there has been much controversy on the subject. For example, Lord Kelvin believed that the jump was entirely located at the surface 1, the interface between the two metals, the jumps and therefore the double layers on 2 and 3 vanishing. Maxwell and Heaviside, on the other hand, would make the jump at the interface identically zero, except for a small effect to be discussed later, and would distribute the total jump in some way between surfaces 2 and 3. It is obvious that other considerations than those already discussed must be advanced to justify any such detailed partition of the jumps between the various possible locations. Heaviside attempts to find such a further argument in the transformations of energy in a circuit in which a current is flowing and in which there are Volta differences. I believe, however, that any such arguments rest on a misconception and that any requirements as to energy transformations automatically adjust themselves in conformity to whatever special assumption is made about the distribution of the potential jumps between the three possible localities, and that no additional information whatever can be obtained from the energy requirements. The situation well repays careful examination.

Let us in the first place assume a double layer at the interface between A and B and see what is involved. The system is supposed in static equilibrium, with no current flowing across the junction. Physically we do not have infinite quantities, so that actually we do not have two layers of infinite surface density of positive and negative electricity separated by an infinitesimal distance, but we have concentrations of positive and negative electricity of high densities separated by distances small compared with the distances involved in ordinary measurements. In the region between the positive and negative charges there must be an intense electric field. If electricity passes from A to B, this field does work on the electricity of amount equal to the product of quantity of electricity and the total potential change associated with the field. Call this potential change V. Now let a steady current flow across the boundary. We assume that this has no effect on the potential jump at the boundary; the evidence for this can of course only be indirect, and rests on the fact that no difference in the Volta potential difference between metals is observed when a current is flowing. I imagine that this point has not been very carefully examined experimentally. However, the point is not important for our present purposes, for the following considerations would still apply even if the potential jump were a function of current. The point is that an electric current flowing across the interface must continually receive energy from the electric field, and the question is where does this energy come from? In solid metals there is no material change accompanying current flow such as there is in a battery, and therefore no apparent source of energy. This led Heaviside to argue that since there is no source of energy there can be no potential jump. It is true that there is a small reversible heating effect at the interface, the Peltier heat, so that there is a continual inflow of thermal energy, but this effect is of a smaller order of magnitude than that corresponding to the Volta jump, and Heaviside did, as a matter of fact, assume a potential jump corresponding to this thermal effect. We return to this thermal effect later in discussing the thermo-electric circuit; for the present we neglect it.

There is nevertheless a source of energy detectable by ordinary physical measuring instruments which Heaviside neglected, and which exactly meets the requirements; this is the energy carried by the Poynting vector. Let the two metals A and B take the form of two cylindrical wires of radius a. Just outside the surface of the wire, girdling the transition zone from one metal to the other, there is an intense electric field parallel to the axis of the wire. The intensity of this field is of course such that its product into the width of the transition zone gives the characteristic Volta difference V_{AB}. If the field is $\mathcal{E}$ in the direction from A to B and the width of the zone Δl, then $\mathcal{E}\Delta l = -V_{AB}$. When electric current flows in the wire there is in addition a circumferential magnetic field at every point external to the wire of amount $H = 2\,i/a$. Over the transition zone magnetic and electric vectors are at right angles and together determine a Poynting vector, $S = \dfrac{\mathcal{E} \times H}{4\,\pi}$, directed normally into the wire. The total inward flow of energy carried by the Poynting vector is the product of its magnitude and the total area across which it acts, which is $2\,\pi a\Delta l$. Substituting the values for $\mathcal{E}$ and H, we find that the total inward flow of energy carried by the Poynting vector is iV_{AB} in unit time. This expression holds no matter what assumption is made about the distribution of the potential jumps between the three possible surfaces. If we assume that the total Volta jump is situated at the interface between the two metals, so that the V of the last paragraph is equal to V_{AB}, then the total work done on the current by the forces at the interface is exactly provided for by the inflow along the Poynting vector, and Heaviside's objection is met.

Let us now suppose that the jumps which together make the Volta jump are situated on two surfaces, one the metallic interface and the other the external surface of B separating it from empty space. Then in the double layer surrounding B there is an intense electric field normal to the surface. When current flows, the magnetic field is circumferential as before; the two together produce a Poynting vector which now points along the axis of the wire. The total Poynting flux coming in from outside space into the girdle about the transition zone now splits; part of it turns and runs in a sheath along the surface of the wire, and the rest penetrates into the interspace between the two metals.

Detailed calculation shows at once that the modified amount now penetrating into the interspace is exactly equal to the modified demands of the electric forces at the interface. Of course the energy flowing along the wire in a sheath escapes into the surrounding space at the other junction between A and B, for in a complete circuit there must be another junction. If the total Volta jump is supposed to be divided in any possible way between the three possible surfaces, or if other metals are introduced into the circuit, it will be found that in every case the Poynting flow automatically takes up the correct distribution. No information whatever can be obtained about the distribution of the potential jumps from energy considerations.

We next have to ask what happens to the energy transferred by the electric forces to the electricity as it crosses the interface. The dimensions make it obvious that we cannot think that this energy is associated with the electricity in virtue of the fact that it constitutes a current, for the energy transferred is a definite amount *per unit quantity of electricity*, not per unit current. Electricity in the metal B must therefore have a different energy from that in A; the precise amount of this difference of energy depends on the assumption that we make about the potential jump at the interface. Maxwell and Heaviside would say that the energy difference is zero except for a small effect of the magnitude of the Peltier heat. Of course the particular value which we will prefer for this energy difference depends on what particular detailed theory we adopt of the electrical constitution of a metal; it is not the place now, while we are dealing only with general considerations, to consider further what this may be. It is to be emphasized, however, that we have already been forced to recognize the existence of effects which amply provide for such possible energies of position of electricity inside a metal. We have had to assume non-electric forces at the surface of a metal to keep an electric charge from being blown off the surface; if there are similar non-electric forces at the interface between two metals, as there may perfectly well be, there will be of necessity a difference of energy of electricity in the two metals. We have seen that the assumption of spatially distributed electricity involves the possibility of internal stresses in the distribution; there may well be effects analogous to differences of internal pressure of the electricity in the two metals, which would involve a difference of energy. We even admit the possibility, if the electrical forces are unopposed in the passage of electricity across the boundary, that electricity may arrive in *B* with a greater kinetic energy than in *A*, so that the difference of energy in *A* and *B* may correspond to a difference of kinetic energy of concealed motions in the electricity.

It will perhaps pay to stop for a moment to make one general comment on what we have been doing in the last few pages. In talking about the Poynting flow at points inside a double layer, or in following the motion of the electricity in the interior of a solid metal across the interface, we have evidently ceased to deal with things directly accessible to measurement, and are therefore in the realm of constructions. We have, however, talked about and calculated with these constructions just as if they were tangible physical things. The only comment to be made on this situation is that we are justified in thus handling our constructions because they have been made with this requirement in view. We do not regard a construction as sufficiently justified to warrant retaining it unless we can perform mental operations with it just as we have above, just exactly as if the construction were accessible to direct measurement. If we get into trouble in doing this, we either discard the construction, or try to modify the physical picture back of the construction so that it will not lead to an inconsistency. Just what requirements we make of our constructions are usually not submitted to detailed analysis, but have to be judged by the context and the physical feeling that every physicist acquires as his experience ripens. It would lead us very far afield to attempt to stop for a detailed analysis of the requirements that we put on our constructions. The requirements made of the constructions that we shall employ here are as easy to analyze out of the context as in any other theoretical discussion of physics, and there is no more reason to anticipate trouble because of them.

Another general matter will pay for careful examination, namely, the way in which we have to handle potential energy in dealing with electrical problems. Great confusion is easy and common here because of a fundamental difference between the rôle of potential energy in electrical systems and in gravitational systems, which are often appealed to in reasoning by analogy in the attempt to reduce the electrical problem to one of greater familiarity. We examine two problems, first a gravitational one, and then the corresponding electrical one.

Consider water in a pipe with two right-angled bends in a gravitational field, as shown in Figure 5. It is in equilibrium under

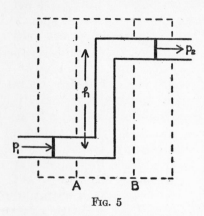

Fig. 5

the action of two pistons, as shown. Imagine the pipe contained in a closed box, and the pistons reaching into it from outside and manipulated from outside. The upper and lower pistons experience different pressures, p_2 and p_1, when the system is in equilibrium. p_1 is greater than p_2 by the pressure due to the head of water, or $p_1 = p_2 + h$. Now push the lower piston in by unit distance and simultaneously withdraw the upper by the same amount. The system inside the box gains energy in amount equal to the difference of work done by the two pistons, or $\Delta E = p_1 - p_2 = h$. This energy change must be associated with some permanent change inside the box. Examination of the contents of the box discloses the transfer of water from a lower to a greater height, and the increase of energy of the system is evidently described by saying that the water in it has acquired greater potential energy of position in the gravitational field. Now divide the box into three parts by the partitions A and B, and consider what account we shall give in detail of the energy transformation. It is obvious that there is no change in the middle third of the box, between A and B. Water has left the left-hand third and entered the right-hand third; we must evidently say that the left-hand third has lost a certain amount of energy and the right-hand third has gained an amount greater by h, the total increase of energy of the system. What is the process by which the left-hand third loses energy and the right-hand third gains it? The left-hand third gains energy in amount p_1, because the piston moves into it, exerting a force p_1, and doing work equal to the product of force and displacement. Similarly the right-hand third loses energy p_2, because the piston moves out, receiving this amount of work. But since p_1 is greater than p_2, this account of the situation would represent the left-hand third as gaining energy instead of the right-hand third. There must be other factors, and these evidently are associated with the motion of the water across the partitions A and B. What energy is convected by the water to give the correct total energy transformation? It is obvious in the first place that there must be a term arising from the potential energy in the gravitational field. This is arbitrary in amount, only differences being significant. Call the potential energy of unit mass in the left-hand compartment h_0 and in the right-hand one $h_0 + h$. Then the left-hand third loses energy h_0 and the right-hand gains $h_0 + h$. But now consider the middle third. Because of convection this gains energy h_0 at the lower end and loses $h_0 + h$ at the upper end, making a net loss of h, unless there are other factors. But since we have already seen that the net change of energy of the middle third must be zero, there must be other factors. Consideration discloses this missing effect in the pv energy of a liquid, familiar in thermodynamics. A liquid in which there is a pressure p convects energy in amount pv with it when moving across a surface. Does this give the desired null net effect at the middle third? The middle third now gains at the left-hand partition the energy $p_1 + h_0$, and loses at the right-hand partition $p_2 + (h_0 + h)$. These two are equal because of the relation between the pressures, and the necessary condition at the middle third is satisfied. The left-hand third now gains the net amount $p_1 - [p_1 + h_0] = - h_0$, and the right-hand third gains $- p_2 + [p_2 + h_0 + h]$, making the net gain by the entire system h, as it should be.

This seems to be the only way of accounting for the energy changes in the gravitational system. The point to be emphasized is that we are driven to associate with the liquid a potential energy in the gravitational field, which it convects with it.

Consider now an analogous electrical arrangement. Imagine an electrically neutral pipe filled with electrically charged balls, capable of moving without friction in the pipe. The whole is placed in a uniform electric field provided by a parallel plate condenser, the plates of which are so far apart that any reaction of the charged balls back on the distribution of charge on the plates may be neglected. The balls tend to fall out of the pipe in the direction of the electrical force, and may be restrained by pistons at the ends, which exert pressures differing by the amount of the electric force. The electric field is supposed so intense that the mutual forces of repulsion between the balls vanish in comparison with the forces of the external field. The electric field produces a pressure gradient along the line of balls exactly like the pressure gradient in the water in the gravitational case. Now displace the pistons and consider the energy changes. The pistons do exactly the same work as in the gravitational case. But there is an important difference elsewhere. As the electrified balls move they constitute an electrical current, which gives rise to a magnetic field, which in conjunction with the electric field produces at every point of space a Poynting flow of energy. Measuring instruments stationed on the outside of the box would disclose the existence of this Poynting flow. Detailed analysis somewhat like that already applied to the problem of the Volta jump of potential will now show that the net inflow on the Poynting vector into the entire system exactly balances the work done by the pistons, so that the net increase of energy inside the box is zero, contrary to the gravitational case. What detailed account shall we give of this? It is obvious, as before, that the middle third of the box can receive no net energy, because there has been no change of anything inside it. But the detailed analysis shows that the net flow into the system on the Poynting vector is confined to the middle third. There must then be a compensating net effect due to the flow of electricity. In the gravitational case the net energy convected into the middle third by the field was zero. Hence if the net convection is the same in the two cases the details must be different. In general we would be prepared to say that the energy convected by the electricity comprises a pressure part and a potential energy part. A few trials, however, will at once convince one that the only way of meeting all the requirements is to discard the potential energy contribution, and say that the electricity convects with it only the energy corresponding to stress, or pv. The left-hand third now gains work from the piston and loses an exactly equal amount of pv energy convected out of it by the electricity; the right-hand third loses work to the piston and gains an exactly equal amount of pv energy convected into it by the electricity, and the middle third gains work from inflow along the Poynting vector and loses an exactly equal amount which is the net difference of the convected pv energies of the electricity at entrance and exit.

The essential difference between the two cases is therefore that in the electrical case we can ascribe no convected energy of position in the *electrostatic* field to the electricity as it moves about. The difference arises quite obviously because in the gravitational case there is no vector corresponding to the Poynting vector. In the electrical case the electricity is entirely neutral in the field, merely an intermediary link through which energy gets transferred from one position or form to another, but not itself the seat of electrical energy. The work done by the pistons in our electrical example is transferred to the field surrounding the system by the mediary of the Poynting vector, and is not to be regarded as stored up inside the box. This essential difference between the two cases is quite often lost sight of in reasoning by analogy from the gravitational to the electrical case.

Physically the state of affairs is much more satisfactory for the electrical than for the gravitational system. If we explore the material inside the box before and after the motion of the pistons, there is no known instrument that will disclose a change of energy, for absolute position in a uniform field makes no difference in physical properties. We are driven, therefore, to associate with gravitating matter a store of energy which can be disclosed by no known measuring instrument. In the electrical system, the energy is obviously in the field, as shown by measurable modifications in the field. The gravitational case is so unsatisfactory that one is strongly tempted to postulate the existence of a new effect not yet discovered corresponding to the Poynting vector, and to search for it experimentally. However, it is well known that there are difficulties connected with the conditions at infinity not yet surmounted in attempting to localize energy in the gravitational field, which would apparently be necessary if the analogue of the Poynting vector for gravitation exists.

One may, if one prefers, entirely ignore the Poynting vector and then say that an electric charge has potential energy of position in an electric field, analogous to gravitational energy of position, and that no electrical energy of position is stored in the field. If consistently carried through, this must give the same result as the other method, but I feel it to be dangerous, and in the following I shall explicitly deal with the Poynting vector.

By way of illustration, consider what account we shall give of the energy transformations when current flows across the interface between two metals at which there

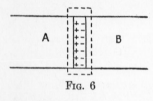

FIG. 6

is assumed to be a potential jump, as in Figure 6. Let us consider the energy balance of a region embracing this interface. Since the state of affairs is steady, and since there are no material changes within the region, we must say that the net energy flow into the region vanishes, irrespective of what point of view we take about the Poynting vector. Let us first describe the situation recognizing the Poynting vector. There is an energy flow into the region on this vector, so that there must be a corresponding net convection of energy out of the region by the current, or the electricity as it flows away on the B side must have a greater intrinsic energy than the electricity which enters on the A side. This excess of intrinsic energy in B must be described as non-electrical, because with a Poynting vector electricity does not have energy of position in an electric field. Now ignore the Poynting vector. Electricity flowing through from A to B passes through an intense electric field, and is now to be described as carrying out with it a smaller potential energy of position in the field than that with which it entered. But since the net inflow is zero, the electricity must carry away with it a compensating greater energy due to its presence in B than that with which it entered due to its presence in A. In either case, therefore, the electricity has to be assigned a *non-electrical* energy of position in the metal. This difference of non-electrical energy can in principle be disclosed by measuring instruments, for surely it is possible to recognize by measuring instruments a difference between metals A and B.

So far all our considerations have been from the classical point of view which considered electricity as a uniformly distributed fluid, a point of view that found its culminating expression in the Maxwell field equations. But of course no physicist can forget that the picture of electricity as a continuous fluid was presently displaced by the picture which represented it to be composed of indivisible particles, and all his thinking about electricity is unavoidably colored by his conception of the electronic structure of electricity. It is too early as yet to tell how this electronic picture will eventually be modified by wave mechanics, which pictures electricity again as having under some conditions properties analogous to a continuous fluid, but there can be no question that very broad aspects of the electronic picture will continue to prove more useful than the continuous medium picture of Maxwell, and we must therefore inquire what modification the electronic picture will introduce into our point of view. Since the point of view of this book is purposely almost exclusively the large-scale point of view which is embraced in Maxwell's equations, the electronic point of view can make little formal difference. Our careful consideration of these fundamental matters has been given not so much in order to enable us to make a direct attack on the question of the correctness of the electronic pictures, as rather to enable us to inquire whether the conventional large-scale descriptions are themselves adequate. Of course if the large-scale descriptions prove inadequate, the electronic pictures devised to explain them must be modified.

In spite of the fact that the electronic point of view does not compel any striking changes in our formal descriptions, nevertheless recognition of it essentially modifies our feeling for certain situations, and it will pay us to examine the matter a little in detail.

Consider the fundamental matter of the electric field at a point. We defined the field as the limit of the ratio of force to charge as the charge is made vanishingly small. But if electricity is atomic in structure, we cannot use a test charge smaller than a single electron, and the definition, from a physical point of view, becomes merely academic. Now the reason for making the test charge vanishingly small is that it by itself affects the distribution of electricity whose field we are trying to measure. If we could in some way freeze every electrical charge in position, so that it could not move under the influence of the test charge, then we could perfectly well define the field as the force on unit charge, provided this charge was concentrated in sufficiently small volume. Or if we choose to use the electron as the exploring body, as we do in many mental experiments, then the field is merely the ratio of the force on the electron to its charge, all other charges being frozen in position and unaffected by the presence of the electron. Now the charge on the electron is so small that as long as it remains at a distance from other bodies beyond the reach of ordinary measuring instruments no appreciable rearrangement of charge is produced by its presence, and the force on the electron gives a sufficiently good measure of the field. But there are conditions under which the electron may get so close to the distribution as to produce important rearrangements of charge, so that the actual force on the electron does not measure the field of the original distribution. The best known and the most important of such situations is when an electron approaches very close to an infinite conducting plane surface. The mathematical treatment from the continuous medium point of view is well known. The approaching charge induces on the plane a charge of opposite sign, which heaps up on the nearer parts of the surface and exerts an attraction. The total net attraction is the same as that which would be exerted by the optical image of the charge in the plane, and is $e/4\,x^2$, where x is the distance between charge and plane. This force is called the "image force." When we get to electronic dimensions, there cannot, of course, be a smooth distribution of heaped-up charge beneath the approaching electron, but at sufficient distances the quivering atoms of positive charge are supposed to give an effect which on the average over a sufficient interval of time approaches closely enough to the mathematical image force. The magnitude of this image force becomes already inappreciable in comparison with others at distances of the order of 10^{-6} cm, so that for ordinary purposes it is negligible, but if the electron should actually come out through the surface, as it does, for example, in phenomena of thermionic emission, then the image force may become important. In fact, if x goes actually to zero, the image force goes to infinity, and its potential also goes to infinity, which would mean an infinite amount of work to get an electron out through the surface against its own image force. But we do not have infinite forces or infinite energies in nature. At close distances the situation is saved by the atomic structure of matter, or even by the finite size of the electron itself. We need not trouble at present about the details of the behavior at short range. The important point for us is that from the point of view of the large-scale equations, and the definition of the electric field which demands that the charges be frozen in position, there is no room for the image force nor for the work done by it when the electron leaves the surface. From the large-scale point of view this force and the corresponding work must be described as non-electrical, although from the electron point of view they are obviously electrical origin. The importance of clearly distinguishing between the two sorts of force is evident; the electrostatic field of the large-scale smooth equations is conservative, and no net work can be received from the field on taking the electron around a closed path. On the other hand, there is no such condition on the image force, and net work may be received from such forces in a closed circuit. In the following, in order to avoid confusion, when we deal with the conservative forces of the large-scale smooth distribution, we shall speak of the "electrostatic" field, and the "electrostatic" potential, instead of merely "electric" field and potential. By doing this we do not fail to recognize that when there are moving parts in the system, as in a dynamo, the large-scale smooth electric field need not be conservative, but we shall not encounter such cases in this book, and no confusion will thereby result. The image force may be referred to as a "non-electrostatic" force.

It is apparent that whenever an electron moves from one region to another physically different from it there may be accompanying rearrangements of the surrounding distributions of other charges, leaving open the possibility of forces analogous to the image force, so that there may be non-electrostatic forces and non-electrostatic work under such conditions. In particular, when current passes across the interface separating two metals, such forces may be called into existence. The existence of such non-electrostatic forces is consistent with the necessity which we have already recognized of a "non-electric" difference of energy of position in the two metals. In the future, in order to avoid confusion, it will be well to refer to this as a "non-electrostatic" difference of energy of position.

Such "non-electrostatic" forces are seen to be capable of accounting for various kinds of phenomena. Thus the motion accompanying the rearrangement of the other charges as an electron is carried about must react with the thermal motion which all charges normally have, so that associated thermal effects are possible. Or in an electron gas, the collisions of the electrons are resisted by the mutual forces of repulsion as they approach closely together, so that the pressure in an electron gas arises from forces eventually electrical in origin, but which from the large-scale point of view must be described as "non-electrostatic." In the body of the metal we may similarly anticipate effects analogous to stresses in electricity, but of non-electrostatic nature. It is further most important to notice that although such non-electrostatic forces are eventually of electrical origin, they may vary greatly in their modes of action. Thus the work done on an electron against the image force as it leaves the surface of a metal is merely the integral of force into displacement, like an ordinary electrostatic force, whereas the work done by the pressure in an electron gas when the gas is displaced is pdv, where dv is the volume expansion of the gas, and has no necessary connection with its displacement. This difference in the various possible ways in which the non-electrostatic forces can do work may prove vital.

CHAPTER II

THERMO–ELECTRIC PHENOMENA

Construct a circuit of two wires of different homogeneous metals A and B and maintain the junctions between A and B at different temperatures τ_1 and τ_0. A current will be found to flow in this circuit; this current may be measured by the magnetic field surrounding the wire, or by a galvanometer so inserted in the circuit that its two binding posts are at the same temperature, or in any other convenient way, such perhaps as by breaking the circuit and connecting the broken ends to the opposite plates of a condenser of sufficiently large capacity. Whatever the measuring instrument, it must be so inserted into the circuit as to be all at the same temperature, so that there may be no complications from thermo-electric phenomena in the measuring instrument.

A current produced in this way in a circuit of two different metals is called a thermo-electric current, and the circuit giving rise to it a thermo-couple. Study of the current produced by such a thermo-couple under various conditions shows that the couple must be recognized to be the seat of an E.M.F. by which the current is produced. As long as the two junctions are at the same temperatures the effective E.M.F. remains constant to a high degree of precision. The thesis that the E.M.F. depends only on the temperatures of the two junctions and does not, in particular, depend on the way in which temperature is distributed between the two junctions, is known as the law of Magnus. It has been called in question by a great many experiments, but most of the apparent failures of the law have been traced to lack of sufficient homogeneity in the metals. It is certainly possible, however, by using for the two branches of the couple unicrystalline wires of the same metal but with different orientations with respect to the principal crystal axis, to produce thermo-currents in a circuit composed of a single metal, and that in its state of most perfect homogeneity. It is obviously necessary, therefore, to modify the original statement of the law of Magnus to the statement that in a thermo-couple composed of a homogeneous and isotropic metal, which means in practise a metal crystallizing in the cubic system, the total E.M.F. depends only on the temperature of the two junctions, and we shall in the future, unless specifically dealing with crystals, assume such isotropic and homogeneous metal. We must recognize that in principle no couple composed of solid metals can be entirely in the condition demanded by the law, because there are stresses and strains in any solid metal in which there is a temperature gradient, and no metal in which there are varying stresses can be called homogeneous. Similarly if we are dealing with couples whose branches are liquid metals, we must recognize the possibility of effects arising from pressure gradients in the liquid. All such effects are very small, however, and negligible for our purposes.

Even with the proviso, however, that the metal be isotropic and free from stress, there is not yet completely unanimous acceptance of the law of Magnus. In particular, Benedicks [1] claims the existence of certain thermo-electric effects not generally considered, the most important of which is a "homogeneous thermo-electric effect," which is a temperature difference in the steady state between the ends of a long uniform wire carrying a steady current. I personally have not been able to verify the existence of this effect, and am doubtful of its existence.* In any event,

---

* Since my experiments yielding a negative result for the "Benedicks" effect have never been published in detail, the following brief account is given.

A loop of constantan wire about 1.0 mm in diameter and 4 m total length was used, the distance between the two parallel arms of the loop being about 5 cm. The central meter of the wire was protected by a heavy brass tube, which was exhausted to 6 mm pressure in order to avoid disturbances due to air currents arising from the heating effects of the current. A differential thermo-couple of 12 junctions was stretched between two points 50 cm from the entrance and the exit ends of the loop. Currents as high as 0.67 amp were used. The method was to search for a change of temperature difference on reversing current. No drift of temperature on reversing current greater than 5×10^{-5} Centigrade degrees in two minutes could be detected. This is about one twenty-fifth of the effect which the data of Benedicks would lead one to expect.

even if the effect exists, it must be very small, and would require
highly special methods for its demonstration; I shall not consider it in the following.

The E.M.F. of a thermo-couple composed of metals A and B
with junctions at temperatures τ_1 and τ_0, τ_1 being the higher
temperature, we shall write as $E_{AB}(\tau_1, \tau_0)$. The order of the subscripts indicates that the E.M.F. is in such a direction that positive current flows from A to B at the hot junction. The E.M.F.
of a couple satisfies two important additive relations. The first
is:

$$E_{AB}(\tau_1, \tau_0) = E_{AB}(\tau_1, \tau_2) + E_{AB}(\tau_2, \tau_0), \qquad \text{II, 1.}$$

where τ_2 is any temperature, intermediate or not between τ_1 and
τ_0. This formula expresses that the sum of the E.M.F.'s of the
two couples of Figure 7 a is the same as
that of the single couple of Figure 7 b,
and is an illustration of the general fact,
demanded by the second law of thermodynamics, that no energy changes arising
from thermal effects are produced by rearrangements of systems in localities all
at the same temperature. Evidently the
energy received by unit quantity of electricity when carried in succession around
the two circuits of Figure 7 a is the same
as that received when carried around the
single circuit of Figure 7 b.

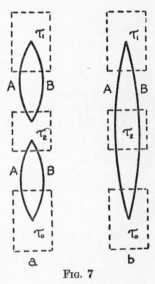

Fig. 7

It is an obvious consequence of this
additive relation that the E.M.F. of a
couple reaching from a lower temperature τ to an upper temperature $\tau + 1$ is
the same as the derivative with respect
to the upper temperature of a couple
reaching from a lower temperature τ_0 to an upper temperature
τ, and this derivative in its turn is independent of the temperature of the lower junction. This derivative, or the E.M.F. of a
couple with unit difference of temperature, is often called the
thermo-electric power, and may be written $e_{AB}(\tau)$.

The second additive relation is:

$$E_{AB}(\tau_1, \tau_0) + E_{BC}(\tau_1, \tau_0) = E_{AC}(\tau_1, \tau_0). \qquad \text{II, 2.}$$

This is what might be expected, the metal B appearing in the two couples corresponding to E_{AB} and E_{BC} in the identical way except for the sign. If, therefore, the contribution which the metal B makes to the total E.M.F. is distributed throughout it in a way depending only on the temperature, and independent of the presence in the circuit of other metals, the action will cancel when the two couples of Figure 8 are joined, and the relation follows. It is the analogue of the Volta law of tensions.

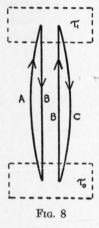

FIG. 8

Obvious consequences are that there is no E.M.F. in a couple all of the same metal, no matter what its temperature distribution, and that the E.M.F. of a couple is not altered by breaking it and inserting into it any third metal, provided the two junctions with the third metal are at the same temperature. With this precaution, galvanometers, or motors to extract mechanical work from the E.M.F., may be inserted into the thermo-electric circuit.

The source of the energy which may be extracted from a thermo-couple when electricity is allowed to flow around it is thermal; this must obviously be the case, since there are no material changes accompanying the flow of current, and there is no other source. The thermal effects which are responsible for the energy manifestations are of two sorts, located in the junctions between the two metals, and located in the single and isotropic metals in the regions where there is a temperature gradient.

Consider first the junctions. When current is allowed to flow in a thermo-couple, it is found that the temperature of the junctions changes unless heat is artificially supplied or abstracted. The rate at which heat must be supplied to the junction to maintain its temperature constant is proportional to the current, and reverses sign when the direction of current flow changes. It is, therefore, in no way like a heat due to an overcoming of resistance, which is proportional to the square of the current. This heat is called the Peltier heat. It depends only on the two metals and the temperature of the junction, and is independent of the nature of the other parts of the circuit. When a current passes across a junction from A to B at a definite temperature, there is always the same absorption or generation of heat at the junction independent of whether the current is driven by an external agency, or whether it is the current that spontaneously flows in the thermo-couple itself. If the direction of current flow reverses, the sign of the heat effect reverses, independent of the reason for the reversal. We denote the Peltier heat by $P_{AB}(\tau)$, indicating that the junction is between the two metals A and B and at temperature τ. A positive sign will be taken to mean that heat must flow into the junction from the surroundings in order to maintain temperature constant when positive current flows from A to B at the junction. We express this by saying that the current absorbs heat at the junction when flowing from A to B. The complete reversibility of P, which means analytically that it must be expressible in terms of odd powers of the current, is assumed in all theoretical discussions. The reversibility has been checked by experiment with an accuracy which is continually improving. It is not impossible, however, that there may be some irreversible effects, but we shall ignore them in this discussion. It is to be noted that any effects at the junction involving even powers of the current, and therefore irreversible, can be described in terms of a resistance at the junction, a function of the current if necessary, and can therefore be treated by the usual methods for dealing with non-ohmic resistances. With regard to the reversible part of the heat, there is no experimental evidence that the Peltier heat departs from strict proportionality to the current, so that the first-power term in the current will be assumed to be sufficient in this discussion, where any assumption has to be made at all.

The Peltier heat is in general a function of temperature; this means that when current flows in a thermo-couple, the heat inflow at one junction is not in general balanced by the heat outflow at the other, so that there is a net appearance or disappearance of heat. We have here evidently a possible source of the energy that drives the current. When thermo-electric effects were first discovered, it was thought that the net Peltier heat was the only source of electrical energy. By comparing the net Peltier heat with the product of E.M.F. and quantity of electricity, it should have been possible to check this idea. Actually, however, this was not done, since the direct measurement of the Peltier heat is not a particularly easy matter, and it was many years before direct measurements of it were made with any accuracy. The correctness of the idea was examined by indirect methods, however, by Lord Kelvin, at that time Sir William Thomson. He applied a thermodynamical argument, which we shall consider in detail presently, and deduced from it that if the Peltier heat were the only source of energy, the E.M.F. of a thermo-couple should be a linear function of absolute temperature. Experimentally this was far from the truth, and Kelvin was therefore driven to postulate the existence of other sources of energy. The only evident such source is in the body of the metal, where there is a temperature gradient. If there is such an effect, Kelvin showed that the temperature distribution in the wire should be altered by the flow of current. The effect to be expected was small, almost beyond the reach of the temperature-measuring instruments of the time, but after a number of attacks on the problem extending over several years, Kelvin was able to establish the existence of the effect. The heat inflow involved in this effect is called the Thomson heat. The original papers of Kelvin reveal the inspiring tenacity with which he clung to his conviction of the existence of this effect in the face of discouraging experimental conditions.

The existence of a Thomson heat means that when a current flows in a metal between two points at a difference of temperature, the temperature distribution will in general be disturbed. The temperature can be forced to maintain its original distribution only by the artificial supply or abstraction of heat from the metal. The amount of extra heat which must be thus supplied when unit quantity of electricity flows from a point at one temperature to a point one degree higher is by definition the Thomson heat at the mean temperature, and is denoted by the letter σ. It is in general a function of metal and temperature. Thus $\sigma_A(\tau)$ denotes the additional heat supplied by the environment per degree temperature difference in the metal A at mean temperature τ when unit quantity of electricity flows up the temperature gradient. This heat is additional to the Joulean heat developed in overcoming the resistance; the Joulean heat can be allowed for by independent measurements of resistance as a function of temperature. If this definition of the Thomson heat corresponds to the experimental facts and is not academic or trivial, it implies that this heating effect reverses sign when the direction of current flow changes, so that we should again be dealing with a reversible phenomenon. This does indeed correspond to the facts as far as they have been established experimentally, but the accuracy with which the reversibility of the Thomson heat has been proved by direct experiment is much less than the corresponding accuracy for the Peltier heat, and there is doubtless room for further experimental work here. Neither is there any experimental evidence at present for a dependence of Thomson heat on current strength, which means that these heating effects double when the current doubles.

The mutual relations between these heating effects and the method of measuring them may now be made more precise. Construct a thermo-couple of metals A and B stretching from τ_0 to τ_1. Break the wire of B and maintain the broken ends at some intermediate temperature τ. Heat flows along the wires down the temperature gradient by thermal conduction. Imagine the wires lagged so that there is no lateral loss of heat. If the wires are not lagged, the lateral loss may be allowed for by independent blank experiments. When the steady state is reached, there are certain thermal inputs or outputs in the three regions τ_0, τ, and τ_1, and a certain temperature distribution is set up in the wire. These quantities are measured. The broken ends of the wire B are now joined, permitting current to flow. We can imagine these ends to be joined through a motor in the box at temperature τ. By allowing the motor to run at various speeds, thus exerting different back E.M.F.'s in the circuit, the current may be varied. It is now found in general that the temperature distribution in the wires and the heat inputs at the three reservoirs have been altered. We find that the original temperature distribution in the wires may be restored by the artificial injection into the wire of suitable amounts of heat at every point of it, and by suitably modifying the inflow at the reservoirs, the reservoirs of course being maintained at the original temperatures. The modified heat inputs to maintain the original distribution are found to be unique, and we suppose that they have been determined by measurement. The Peltier heats are now the difference between the final and the original heats supplied by the reservoirs (this effect at the intermediate reservoir τ vanishes), and the Thomson heats are the heats supplied at every point of the body of the wire, all taken per unit quantity of electricity flowing in the circuit. This neglects the Joulean heat, which may either be allowed for by calculation or may be made to vanish in comparison with the other effects by decreasing the current, the Joulean heat decreasing as the square of the current and the others decreasing as the first power.

The Peltier and the Thomson heats are to be thought of, therefore, as given by a sort of phantom experiment, the difference between two actual ones.

Actually, the idealized experiments just described would be difficult of execution, particularly the requirement that a suitably adjusted amount of heat be fed in laterally to the wire at every point, and the constants P and σ are actually determined in somewhat different ways. For example, the Peltier heat may be determined by the rate at which the junction of two metals A and B changes temperature when current is led across the junction, enlarging the junction so as to make a sort of calorimeter of it, and correcting for the loss of heat by conduction and laterally by suitable blank experiments. The Joulean heating is usually allowed for by reversing the direction of current flow, assuming that the Peltier heat is reversible. The Joulean heat may be calculated, however, and in this way the reversibility of the Peltier heat checked.

The Thomson heat may be determined by measuring the altered temperature distribution when a current of electricity flows in a wire normally carrying a thermal conduction current. We suppose the two ends of the wire maintained at constant temperature difference, and the temperature distribution determined by a sufficient number of thermo-couples situated along the wire so that a smooth curve of temperature as a function of length may be drawn, and thus the temperature gradient determined at every point with and without the electric current. We suppose the wire so lagged that there is no lateral loss. In the absence of electric current the temperature gradient is constant, and there is a uniform flow of heat along the wire. When current flows, the gradient is no longer constant, so that the heat flowing into an element of length is not the same as that flowing out. The difference between the conduction heat flowing in and out is accounted for by the Joulean heat and the Thomson heat inside the element. The net conduction heat flowing out of the region in unit time is $-\kappa_l \Delta x \dfrac{d^2\tau}{dx^2}$, where κ_l is the linear thermal conductivity. The rate of generation of Joulean heat is $i^2 r_l \Delta x$, where r_l is the linear resistance of the conductor, and the rate of absorption of Thomson heat by the current is $i\sigma \Delta x \dfrac{d\tau}{dx}$. The condition of heat balance now gives at once

$$-\kappa_l \Delta x \frac{d^2\tau}{dx^2} = i^2 r_l \Delta x - i\sigma \Delta x \frac{d\tau}{dx}, \text{ or } \sigma = \frac{i^2 r_l + \kappa_l \dfrac{d^2\tau}{dx^2}}{i \dfrac{d\tau}{dx}}. \quad \text{II, 3.}$$

This is the equation actually used in the experimental determination of σ[2]. Ideally the equation contains the possibility of establishing the reversibility of σ by checking it over a wide range of conditions, but actually the effects are so small that the measurements, even under the optimum conditions, do not have a high degree of accuracy.

The equation can obviously be generalized at once for three-dimensional flow, and the thermal conductivity may be allowed to be a function of temperature, giving:

$$i \cdot \sigma \text{ Grad } \tau = i^2 r + \text{Div } (\kappa \text{ Grad } \tau), \quad \text{II, 4.}$$

where r and κ have now the obvious three-dimensional significance.

We are now ready to consider the thermodynamic argument by which Kelvin deduced certain relations between the Peltier and Thomson heats and the E.M.F. of a thermo-couple. Imagine a couple of metals A and B running from absolute temperature τ to $\tau + \Delta\tau$. The E.M.F. of this couple is $\dfrac{dE_{AB}}{d\tau}\Delta\tau$ driving current around the couple from A to B at the hot junction. This is therefore the energy delivered by the E.M.F. when unit current of electricity flows around the circuit. The first law of thermodynamics demands that the source of this energy be the net heat inflow into the system. There are four such heat inflows. There is heat inflow at the hot junction of amount $P_{AB}(\tau + \Delta\tau)$, heat inflow at the cold junction of $P_{BA}(\tau) = -P_{AB}(\tau)$, heat inflow laterally into the metal A in the region of temperature gradient between the junctions of amount $\sigma_A\Delta\tau$, and similar inflow into B of amount $-\sigma_B\Delta\tau$. Equating these two amounts of energy,

$$\Delta\tau \frac{dE_{AB}}{d\tau} = P_{AB}(\tau + \Delta\tau) - P_{AB}(\tau) + (\sigma_A - \sigma_B)\,\Delta\tau.$$

Whence:

$$\frac{dE_{AB}}{d\tau} = \frac{dP_{AB}}{d\tau} + (\sigma_A - \sigma_B). \qquad \text{II, 5.}$$

The equations which have just been deduced obviously apply to our phantom experiment, the difference between two actual ones. But exactly the same equation would have been obtained if we analyze the actual experiment. Imagine the thermo-couple set up in a box, with only the two junctions at $\tau + \Delta\tau$ and τ protruding, and the couple short circuited inside so that all the work of the E.M.F. goes to generating Joulean heat inside the box. When a steady state is reached, heat flows into the box at one place and out at another. The box delivers no work, the only exchange with the environment being thermal. Furthermore, examination of the contents of the box discloses the most important fact that there is no alteration in the physical properties of the contents of the box as time goes on. It must be, therefore, that the total heat flowing into the box is equal to that flowing out, or :

(Heat flowing in at $\tau + \Delta\tau$)   = (Heat flowing out at τ)

Now,

   (Heat flowing in at $\tau + \Delta\tau$) = (Peltier heat flowing in at $\tau + \Delta\tau$)
                  + (conduction heat in at $\tau + \Delta\tau$),

and,

   (Heat flowing out at τ)   = (Peltier heat flowing out at τ)
                  + (conduction heat out at τ).

But the conduction heat flowing out has been augmented over that flowing in by the Joulean heat developed in the metal, and diminished by the Thomson heat absorbed by the current.   Hence

(conduction heat out at τ) = (conduction heat in at $\tau + \Delta\tau$)
$$+ \, i^2R - i(\sigma_A - \sigma_B)\Delta\tau.$$

But

$$i^2R = i \times \text{E.M.F.} = i\,\frac{dE_{AB}}{d\tau}\,\Delta\tau.$$

Substituting these quantities gives an equation from which the conduction heat cancels, leaving exactly the same result as before. That is, equation 5, which is deduced from the law of the conservation of energy, is a rigorous deduction from the actual experiment, and does not apply only to the phantom experiment, although the deduction is simpler if only the phantom experiment is considered.

The first law thus gives one relation connecting Peltier and Thomson heats with E.M.F. A second relation is needed to completely determine these heats ; such a relation could obviously be obtained if there were some way of applying the second law of thermodynamics also.   But application of the second law demands complete reversibility in the phenomena, and these phenomena are obviously not reversible, since there are two essentially irreversible phenomena always present, Joulean heating and thermal conduction.   What Kelvin did was to neglect these irreversible phenomena and consider only the phantom experiment, which deals only with completely reversible phenómena. Statements are sometimes made that the irreversible aspects may be made vanishingly small by suitably changing the dimensions of the circuit. But the matter is not entirely simple, because if, for example, the cross section of the wire is halved, the resistance is doubled, the current halved, and the i^2R loss halved. At the same time the thermal resistance is doubled and the thermal loss halved. But when current is halved, the reversible effects are also halved, so that there is nothing here gained in the ratio of reversible to irreversible effects. We will discuss later what can be done in the way of choosing optimum conditions. Kelvin knew perfectly well, however, that the irreversible aspects could not be made to vanish in any such way, and he explicitly recognized and stated that his application of the second law to the phantom experiment was an assumption, to be justified by the agreement with experiment of the relations thus deduced. At the same time, Kelvin had a pretty vigorous conviction of the correctness of this assumption, as shown by his obstinate persistence in searching for the Thomson heat. This conviction doubtless had back of it the physical feeling that the mechanisms responsible for electrical resistance and thermal conductivity had no connection with the thermo-electric mechanism, as shown by the lack of any apparent correlation between the thermo-electric parameters of various substances and their electrical and thermal resistance.

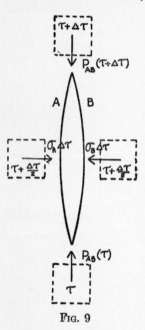

Fig. 9

Let us now apply the second law to the phantom experiment, in which all the effects are entirely reversible. The second law states that the entropy of the entire universe cannot change as long as only reversible effects take place. The universe consists of the thermo-couple and four reservoirs which feed into the couple the heats required for the two Peltier heats and the two Thomson heats, as indicated in Figure 9. Allow unit quantity of electricity to flow around the circuit. Since the effects are reversible, the net entropy of the four reservoirs and of the couple cannot be changed. Detailed examination of the thermo-couple shows absolutely no detectable change in it after the flow of electricity, so that we are bound, by the principle of sufficient reason, to say that there is no change in the entropy of the couple. The net change in the entropy of all the reservoirs must, therefore, vanish. Each reservoir by itself changes in entropy because of heat transfer. The condition for no net change on all four together is obviously:

$$-\frac{P_{AB}(\tau + \Delta\tau)}{\tau + \Delta\tau} + \frac{P_{AB}(\tau)}{\tau} - \frac{\sigma_A \Delta\tau}{\tau + \frac{\Delta\tau}{2}} + \frac{\sigma_B \Delta\tau}{\tau + \frac{\Delta\tau}{2}} = 0$$

The first two terms combine at once to give $-\dfrac{d}{d\tau}\left(\dfrac{P_{AB}}{\tau}\right)\Delta\tau$, so that we obtain at once

$$\frac{d}{d\tau}\left(\frac{P_{AB}}{\tau}\right) + \frac{1}{\tau}(\sigma_A - \sigma_B) = 0. \qquad \text{II, 6.}$$

Now eliminate in succession P_{AB} or $\sigma_A - \sigma_B$ between equations 5 and 6, getting:

$$P_{AB} = \tau \frac{dE_{AB}}{d\tau} \qquad \text{II, 7.}$$

and

$$\sigma_B - \sigma_A = \tau \frac{d^2 E_{AB}}{d\tau^2}. \qquad \text{II, 8.}$$

These equations determine P_{AB} and $\sigma_A - \sigma_B$ in terms of the measured E.M.F. of a thermo-couple as a function of temperature. Measurements of thermal E.M.F. are easy, and this proves to be the simplest method of determining P and σ. The values so obtained should agree with the values obtained by the direct methods already outlined. As long as there is any doubt as to the legitimateness of neglecting the irreversible processes of Joulean heat and thermal conduction, comparison of values obtained by the direct and indirect methods is not superfluous. At present, however, there is no evidence whatever of any discrepancy between the two values, and it is tacitly assumed in most theoretical discussions that neglect of the irreversible processes is justified.

The argument in the form just given is preferable, I believe, to the argument that is sometimes advanced. The thermo-couple is sometimes treated as the analog of an ordinary steam engine, for example, in which the electricity is the analog of the working fluid of the engine. The entropy change of the fluid in a complete working cycle is then put equal to zero, as it must be since the fluid returns to its initial condition. The assumption of reversibility enters in the assumption that the change of entropy of the fluid at various parts of the cycle can be obtained from the corresponding changes in the reservoirs, heat interchange between reservoir and fluid taking place with no gain of entropy because there is no sensible temperature difference. Applied to our example, evidently the same result is obtained as by the argument actually employed. But this treatment is objectionable because in the first place it demands the assumption of details which are not necessary to the thermodynamic argument, and thermodynamics dispenses with details as far as possible. The details in this case furthermore have more or less the character of " constructions," electrical current as a " fluid " not having full experimental status. In the second place, the requirement that the electricity which constitutes the current shall have returned to its initial position has no physical significance, since there is no way of assigning a velocity to the electricity whose motion constitutes the current, or of recognizing the individual parts of the electricity and determining when they have returned to the starting point.

The question of the propriety of neglecting the irreversible phenomena associated with the thermo-electric circuit is of such importance that I consider in more detail two aspects of it. Consider in the first place the results that would be obtained by a rigorous application of thermodynamics, not neglecting the irreversible aspects. Imagine a thermo-couple of two metals A and B reaching from τ to $\tau + \Delta\tau$. Useful work is extracted from the system by inserting a motor with back E.M.F. The length and the cross section of the conductors may be altered, thus changing the resistance and over-all thermal conductivity, and thus also changing the Joulean loss and the heat conducted from one reservoir to another. The dimensions of the circuit and the back E.M.F. are now to be given such values that the ratio of the useful work done against the back E.M.F. to the total increase of entropy of the reservoirs shall be a maximum. With these dimensions for the circuit the thermodynamic condition is written down that $W \leqq Q\dfrac{\Delta\tau}{\tau}$, where W is the useful work, Q the total heat leaving the upper reservoir, τ its temperature, and $\Delta\tau$ the temperature difference of the reservoirs. The result is the inequality:

$$\tau\frac{dE_{AB}}{d\tau} - P_{AB} \leqq 2\,\tau^{\frac{1}{2}}[(r_A\kappa_A)^{\frac{1}{2}} + (r_B\kappa_B)^{\frac{1}{2}}], \qquad \text{II, 9.}$$

where r and κ are the specific electrical resistances and thermal conductivities of the metals, and the metals are so designated that the sign of $\dfrac{dE_{AB}}{d\tau}$ is positive. This relation was deduced by Boltzmann.[3]

The result previously obtained, neglecting irreversibility, corresponds to putting the right-hand side of 9 equal to zero, and using the equality sign. The relation so obtained, $\tau\dfrac{dE}{d\tau} = P$, is approximately satisfied, as a matter of experiment. Certainly the experimental check is good enough to justify the statement that P_{AB} is always positive when $\dfrac{dE_{AB}}{d\tau}$ is positive. Thus, as a matter of experiment, $\tau\dfrac{dE}{d\tau} - P$ is a small quantity, much less than $\tau\dfrac{dE}{d\tau}$ itself. Now an examination of the experimental numerical values shows that in practically every case the right-hand side of 9 is greater than $\tau\dfrac{dE}{d\tau}$. It is therefore all the more greater than $\tau\dfrac{dE}{d\tau} - P$. In fact the difference between the two sides of the inequality is so great that no useful restriction is imposed by it, and in practical application the inequality is without interest.

The wide discrepancy between the numerical magnitude of the quantities on the two sides of the inequality is connected with the very small over-all efficiency of actual thermo-couples. It will be found that no actual couple composed of metals in any feasible range of temperature has an efficiency of more than a fraction of one per cent.

The very great failure of the rigorous thermodynamic inequality to impose any useful restriction on numerical magnitudes cannot help but increase our conviction that it is legitimate to neglect the irreversible aspects of the process, and that Kelvin's relation is justified. It is to be remembered, furthermore, that we would be able by proper choice of the dimensions of the circuit to get rid of either irreversible Joulean heat or thermal conduction taken by itself. It is only because both are present simultaneously that we are in difficulty. In most other cases there is only one irreversible process that has to be made vanishingly small, as for example conduction loss due to a finite temperature difference between source and recipient. The point of view is therefore to a certain extent a most natural one that the fact that we are here concerned with two intrinsically irreversible processes which are so connected that they cannot both be made to vanish simultaneously is more or less fortuitous. The early conviction of Kelvin, however, that the irreversible aspects could be neglected because there was no necessary connection between the mechanisms of thermal and electrical conduction and thermo-electricity had to be given up with the advent of electron theories of metals and the recognition that the electrons were primarily responsible for all three phenomena. It is therefore of great interest that it has proved to be one of the easiest tasks of the electron theory of metals to reproduce Kelvin's thermodynamic relations, in spite of failure to reproduce satisfactorily other important aspects of the experimental situation. This has again led to the apparently widespread conviction that Kelvin's relations are all right.

It seems, therefore, that it is not inconceivable that there might be some way of rephrasing the argument of Kelvin which would justify neglect of the irreversible aspects, or at least make us a little better satisfied to neglect them. It does prove possible, as a matter of fact, to so rearrange the argument by setting up the circuit in such a way that the irreversible effects are a maximum, instead of so that they are a minimum, as did Boltzmann. Imagine a thermally insulated box into which lead two heavy bars of metal A, which are short circuited inside the box by a short block of metal B, as shown in Figure 10. The whole system

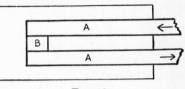

FIG. 10

is initially at constant temperature. Electric current is now led into and out of the box through the external leads of A. We imagine this current delivered by a perfectly efficient dynamo with windings made of the metal A. The entire external circuit is then of one metal, and by hypothesis at constant temperature, so that there are no external heating effects. Passage of the current across the junctions A to B is accompanied by a positive Peltier heat at one junction and a negative heat at the other; one junction will rise in temperature and the other fall. The difference of temperature thus generated between the junctions will be accompanied by a thermal conduction current through B, whose magnitude depends on the temperature difference. The temperature difference between the junctions will obviously rise until the thermal conduction exactly accounts for the Peltier heats at the junctions. There will of course also be conduction from the junctions into the rods A, but as time goes on the quantity of heat escaping in this way becomes vanishingly small in comparison with that conducted directly across B, provided the rods are made long enough. A quasi-steady state is therefore reached, in which the Peltier heats are dissipated in the thermal conduction current across B. Let the final temperature difference between the junctions be $\Delta\tau$, and the current i. The heat iP_{AB} passes by conduction in unit time down a temperature drop $\Delta\tau$. If an ordinary thermal conduction current passes from τ to $\tau - \Delta\tau$, the increase of entropy accompanying passage of amount of heat Q is

$$Q \frac{\Delta\tau}{\tau^2} \left\{ = Q \left(\frac{1}{\tau - \Delta\tau} - \frac{1}{\tau} \right) \right\}.$$

We now introduce the hypothesis that thermal conduction is an essentially irreversible process, always accompanied by its characteristic increase of entropy, whether or not the conduction is accompanied by other processes. This means that in the case of our thermo-couple entropy is increasing, because of irreversible thermal conduction, by the amount $iP_{AB} \dfrac{\Delta\tau}{\tau^2}$ per unit time. This increase of entropy must manifest itself in a rise of temperature of the material inside the box, there being no other possibility. The whole box is therefore slowly rising in temperature, carrying with it the temperature difference $\Delta\tau$ between the junctions. The origin of this rise of temperature is obviously in the neighborhood of the block B, there being no other place. The conduction loss to the outside because of this rise of temperature vanishes if the rods A are made long enough. The rise of temperature of the entire contents of the box is evidently produced by the energy fed into the box by the source of the current, the energy so fed in being entirely converted into thermal effects within the box, since no mechanical work is involved. The energy delivered by the current to the box is $i \dfrac{dE_{AB}}{d\tau} \Delta\tau$, where $\dfrac{dE_{AB}}{d\tau} \Delta\tau$ is the E.M.F. of a couple constituted of metals A and B with junctions at temperature difference $\Delta\tau$. This energy appears as heat at temperature τ, increasing entropy by $\dfrac{1}{\tau} \left[i \dfrac{dE_{AB}}{d\tau} \Delta\tau \right]$. Equating the two entropy changes gives

$$i \frac{P_{AB}}{\tau^2} \Delta\tau = i \frac{\Delta\tau}{\tau} \frac{dE_{AB}}{d\tau}.$$

Whence :

$$\tau \frac{dE_{AB}}{d\tau} = P_{AB}.$$

This is the first of Kelvin's relations; the second follows at once from the first law of thermodynamics, which is certainly applicable whether there is or not irreversibility.

In this argument we have neglected the Thomson heat and the Joulean resistance heating. The effect of the Thomson heat is of a different order, for the total Thomson heat developed in B is $i\sigma_B \Delta\tau$. This escapes by conduction through a temperature difference less on the average than $\Delta\tau$, so that the increase of entropy associated with the Thomson heat in the metal B is less than $i\sigma_B \dfrac{(\Delta\tau)^2}{\tau^2}$, which is thus of a lower order than the increase due to the Peltier heat. The situation with respect to the Thomson heat in A is of course similar. The effect of the Joulean heat exactly adds to the effect already considered, and leaves the final result unchanged. If the resistance of the circuit is R, the Joulean heat is i^2R, and the resulting increase of entropy $\dfrac{i^2R}{\tau}$. But the input E.M.F. must now be greater than before by iR, so that the input energy is greater by i^2R, and the associated entropy increase $\dfrac{i^2R}{\tau}$ exactly cancels the amount just found. By putting the argument in this form the fact that there are two irreversible processes taking place simultaneously introduces no complication.

It cannot be claimed that this is a rigorous deduction of Kelvin's relations using only classical thermodynamics. The hypothesis that the irreversible process of heat conduction and Joulean heating are always accompanied by the same characteristic increase of entropy whether or not accompanied by other processes must be recognized to be a new hypothesis, going beyond any explicit formulation to be found in classical thermodynamics. The new hypothesis seems to be a most natural one, certainly not opposed in spirit to classical thermodynamics, and quite consistent with statistical pictures of the nature of entropy. In fact, the new hypothesis may be usefully used in attacking problems which can also be treated by classical methods, and the fact that it has not been previously explicitly enunciated appears to be more or less accidental. My ideas on this subject have not been accepted by Kennard, however, who sees in thermo-electric phenomena very strong analogies with phenomena of thermal transpiration in gases, which certainly have unremovable irre-

versible aspects. It appears to me that this analogy might justify one in repudiating the fundamental experimental assumption
that Peltier and Thomson heats are *completely* reversible, and in
seeking experimentally for effects involving imperfect reversibility. This I feel to be an entirely defensible position, but,
granted the reversibility, which was fundamental to the argument, I still feel that the considerations above are very plausible.
The matter has been discussed in print,[5] and the reader may
form his own opinion.

The two relations of Kelvin are as much as can be got by application of the first and second laws of thermodynamics. Additional information about the behavior in the neighborhood of 0°
Abs. may be obtained by an application of the third law. We
have at all temperatures $\dfrac{P_{AB}}{\tau} = \dfrac{dE_{AB}}{d\tau}$. The left-hand side represents the entropy change of the junction when current crosses it.
The passage of the current is a reversible phenomenon; the third
law would lead us to expect therefore that this entropy change must
vanish at 0° Abs., or $\dfrac{dE_{AB}}{d\tau} = 0$ at 0° Abs., which is another way of
saying that the thermo-electric power of any couple vanishes at
0°. This expectation is apparently supported by experiment.
Similarly $\dfrac{\sigma_B - \sigma_A}{\tau}$ represents the change of entropy in the body
of the metal in which there is a temperature gradient when cur-
rent flows. If we suppose the temperature gradient maintained
by some agency that suppresses the irreversible flow of heat, then
we may apply the third law here also, which gives $\lim\limits_{\tau \to 0} \dfrac{d^2 E_{AB}}{d\tau^2} = 0$.
The experimental evidence on this point is more difficult, how-
ever, and there would seem to be more uncertainty than with
respect to the first derivative, as indeed there is with respect to
the theoretical argument also.

This is probably as far as we can get by general thermodynamics which does not analyze the details and which deals only
with quantities directly measurable, for it is to be emphasized
that all the quantities of our analysis up to this point, E.M.F.,

Peltier and Thomson heats, are directly measurable. But since in talking about electric currents we have already introduced constructions, such for example, as the electric potential at points inside a metal, it is inevitable that we should seek to go further, and see what service these constructions can do us and what picture they give of internal conditions. How shall we represent the action at an interface between two metals where there is a Peltier heat, or the action in the body of a metal with a temperature gradient where Thomson heat is absorbed?

The conventional account is as follows. When electricity crosses the interface it receives thermal energy from its surroundings. This is described as due to the action of an E.M.F. which delivers in unit time to the current when it crosses the interface an amount of energy equal to the product of current and E.M.F., and this is also equal to iP. The E.M.F. at the interface is therefore equal to the Peltier heat. Normally the force which is involved in the existence of this E.M.F. tends to drive electricity from one metal to the other, and this would produce an infinite current across the interface, since the thickness and therefore the resistance of the interface vanish. But since there is no infinite current, this tendency must be resisted by an equal and opposite electrostatic force, which therefore involves a double layer. The interface is, then, the seat of a double layer of strength equal to P. This double layer is independent of any double layer demanded by the Volta potential difference, and is the only double layer supposed to exist by Heaviside, for example. Similarly in the body of the metal where there is a temperature gradient, the conventional picture sees a distributed e.m.f. of magnitude σ Grad τ per unit length, which is opposed when the circuit is open by an equal and opposite electrostatic force, for otherwise a steady current would flow in the open circuit. On closed circuit the normal internal electrostatic force is diminished by the iR drop.

It seems to me that very grave objections can be made to this picture on perfectly general grounds. If there is an electrostatic double layer and hence an electrostatic difference of potential at the interface, then when current flows there is a Poynting vector carrying energy away from the region of the interface. The analysis is exactly like that for the corresponding Volta difference, and it appears at once that the energy carried away in this way from the interface by the Poynting vector is exactly equal to the Peltier heat. The net inflow into the system from outside at the junction is therefore zero. Similarly there is a Poynting outflow at all points of the homogeneous metal where there is a temperature gradient which exactly neutralizes the inflow of energy as Thomson heat. The result is that there is no net inflow into the complete system, so that there is no source for the energy delivered by the E.M.F. of the complete circuit.

The incorrectness of the conventional point of view I believe can be made absolutely certain if one considers thermo-electric phenomena in single metal crystals of a non-cubic metal. Two wires made of single crystals of such a metal inclined to the axis at different angles behave toward each other exactly like two different metals. In particular, there is a Peltier heat when current passes across an interface at which the orientation of the crystal changes, and the conventional point of view would therefore demand a double layer at the interface equal in magnitude to the Peltier heat. Consider now a crystal block from which a cubically shaped piece has been cut out and replaced in a different orientation, as shown in Figure 11. In the steady state at uniform temperature no currents can flow in the compound block. In passing perpendicularly across the interface from A to B, that is, in passing from a region where one moves parallel to the crystal axis to a region where one is moving perpendicularly, one would, according to the argument above, encounter a discontinuity of potential equal to $P_{\parallel\perp}$. Similarly in passing from C to D, one passes through the same change of orientation, so that the potential at D must be greater than that at C also by $P_{\parallel\perp}$. But C and B are two points inside a homogeneous metal all at the same temperature with no currents flowing, and therefore C and B must be at the same potential. Hence the potential of D exceeds that of A by $2P_{\parallel\perp}$. But D

FIG. 11

and A are also two points in the same homogeneous piece of metal and hence must also be at the same potential. Hence a contradiction, and it follows that the potential of all four points must be equal, and there can be no jump of electrostatic potential at the interface.

Examination shows at once that our difficulty has arisen because we have said that the agent which delivers energy to the electricity is like the force of electrostatics, that is, we have recognized no difference between what we called in chapter I a working E.M.F. and a driving E.M.F. If we recognize the distinction between these two things, the phenomena in a thermo-electric circuit receive an entirely consistent description.

We confine our considerations at first to a couple whose two branches are made of single crystals of the same metal, in one branch the axis being parallel to the length, and in the other perpendicular. If the rods are inclined to the axis at angles other than 0° and 90°, there are other complicating phenomena which will be considered in the special chapter on crystals. The formulas already found for different metals apply without change. In particular, we have at the interfaces Peltier heat of amount $P_{\parallel\perp}$, and in the body of the metal Thomson heats $\sigma_{\parallel}$ and $\sigma_{\perp}$. We have Kelvin's relations.

$$\frac{1}{\tau} P_{\parallel\perp} = \frac{dE_{\parallel\perp}}{d\tau}, \qquad\qquad \text{II, 10.}$$

$$\frac{1}{\tau} (\sigma_{\perp} - \sigma_{\parallel}) = \frac{d^2 E_{\parallel\perp}}{d\tau^2}. \qquad\qquad \text{II, 11.}$$

At the interface thermal energy is absorbed, and therefore there must be a working E.M.F. of magnitude $P_{\parallel\perp}$, as there always is when energy in any form is delivered to the current. But there is no electrostatic potential jump at the interface, and therefore no double layer, and hence by equation I, 4 no driving E.M.F. The driving E.M.F. of the couple must therefore be situated in the body of the metal where there is a temperature gradient. Furthermore, the net driving e.m.f. integrated around the circuit must be such as to equal the directly measured total E.M.F. of the complete circuit, which is also the net working e.m.f. integrated around the circuit, and is equal to the net heat input.* Can we now so distribute an $(e.m.f.)_d$ in the body of the metal as to meet this condition? This can at once be done by integration of equation 11 for $\dfrac{d^2 E_{\parallel\perp}}{d\tau^2}$. Integrate this once, obtaining:

$$\frac{dE_{\parallel\perp}}{d\tau} = \int_{\tau_0}^{\tau} \frac{\sigma_\perp}{\tau}\,d\tau - \int_{\tau_0}^{\tau} \frac{\sigma_\parallel}{\tau}\,d\tau + \text{Const.}$$

The constant may be found from equation 10 on putting $\tau = \tau_0$ and is obviously,

$$\text{Const.} = \frac{dE_{\parallel\perp}}{d\tau}\bigg|_{\tau=\tau_0} = \left(\frac{P_{\parallel\perp}}{\tau}\right)_{\tau=\tau_0}$$

If we put $\tau_0 = 0°$ Abs., the two integrals vanish because their limits coincide, and the constant vanishes by the third law.

Hence $\dfrac{dE_{\parallel\perp}}{d\tau} = \displaystyle\int_0^{\tau} \frac{\sigma_\perp}{\tau}\,d\tau - \int_0^{\tau}\frac{\sigma_\parallel}{\tau}\,d\tau.$ II, 12.

Integrate again, obtaining:

$$E_{\parallel\perp}(\tau,\tau_0) = \int_{\tau_0}^{\tau} d\tau \int_0^{\tau}\frac{\sigma_\perp}{\tau}\,d\tau - \int_{\tau_0}^{\tau} d\tau \int_0^{\tau}\frac{\sigma_\parallel}{\tau}\,d\tau,$$

or, in particular:

$$E_{\parallel\perp}(\tau,\,0) = \int_0^{\tau} d\tau \int_0^{\tau}\frac{\sigma_\perp}{\tau}\,d\tau - \int_0^{\tau} d\tau \int_0^{\tau}\frac{\sigma_\parallel}{\tau}\,d\tau. \qquad \text{II, 13.}$$

* The proof is simple that the integral of $(e.m.f.)_d$ around any line of current flow is always equal to the integral of $(e.m.f.)_w$, or:

$$\int (e.m.f.)_d = \int (e.m.f.)_w.$$

By integrating equation I, 4 we get at once $i = \dfrac{\displaystyle\int (e.m.f.)_d}{R}$, where R is the total resistance of the circuit, because $\int \mathcal{E} = 0$.

Total energy delivered to the current $= i \displaystyle\int (e.m.f.)_w$ (by definition)

$$= i^2 R = i(iR) = i \int (e.m.f.)_d$$

and

$$\int (e.m.f.)_w = \int (e.m.f.)_d \qquad\qquad \text{Q.E.D.}$$

The constant of integration is again zero, because the total E.M.F. of a couple both of whose junctions are at the same temperature is zero.

This expression for the total E.M.F. evidently represents the total as the sum of contributions made by each element of the circuit whose ends are at a temperature difference $d\tau$ of amount $- d\tau \int_0^\tau \frac{\sigma}{\tau} d\tau$, the direction being such as to drive electricity up the temperature gradient, and this is therefore a possible expression for the driving e.m.f. This expression is uniquely determined except for an additive term which must be such as to integrate to zero around a complete circuit. The completely general expression in an element of unit length is therefore :

$$(\text{e.m.f.})_d = - \frac{d\tau}{dx} \left[\int_0^\tau \frac{\sigma}{\tau} d\tau + f(\tau) \right], \qquad \text{II, 14.}$$

where $f(\tau)$ is a temperature function, the same for all metals.

In a linear metallic conductor along which there is a temperature gradient, and which is open circuited so that no current flows, an electrostatic potential gradient is automatically produced by which this driving e.m.f. is neutralized.

The working e.m.f. in any element is given by the heat absorption, and is therefore :

$$(\text{e.m.f.})_w = \sigma \frac{d\tau}{dx}. \qquad \text{II, 15.}$$

The working e.m.f. and the driving e.m.f. in the body of the metal are therefore quite different, and in general are of opposite sign. At the interface there is no driving e.m.f. but there is a working e.m.f. equal to the Peltier heat.

We next seek to account for the energy transformations in the separate elements of the circuit which accompany the flow of current. Imagine a linear conductor in which there is a temperature gradient, and in which a steady current is flowing. Since the state of affairs is steady, the net amount of energy flowing into any element must be zero. We suppose no lateral flow of heat, the Thomson heat requirement of the current being abstracted from the thermal energy of the conductor, and manifesting itself in a rearrangement of the temperature gradient. There are therefore just three ways in which energy can get into an element of the conductor; it may be carried in by the Poynting vector, it may get in by thermal conduction, and it may be convected in by the current. If we call U the energy convected by unit current, then the equation of energy balance is obviously,

$$- \frac{d}{dx} (iU) + \frac{d}{dx} \left(\kappa_l \frac{d\tau}{dx} \right) - i \frac{dV}{dx} = 0, \qquad \text{II, 16.}$$

where the first term is the net energy convected into an element of unit length by the current, the second term is the net heat conducted in, and the third term the net inflow on the Poynting vector, all per unit time.

We may now fasten our attention on the current. This leaves the element with a different amount of energy from that with which it entered. The difference must have been acquired within the region. Within the element the current is concerned in three kinds of action. It absorbs thermal energy from the material of the conductor in amount $i\sigma \frac{d\tau}{dx}$, it delivers Joulean heat to the metal in amount $i^2 r_l$ in flowing against the resistance of the metal, and it receives from the Poynting vector an amount $i\mathcal{E}_x = - i \frac{dV}{dx}$. Setting the net gain equal to the amounts received gives :

$$\frac{d}{dx} (iU) = i\sigma \frac{d\tau}{dx} - i^2 r_l - i \frac{dV}{dx}. \qquad \text{II, 17.}$$

If $\frac{d}{dx} (iU)$ is eliminated between equations 16 and 17, we obtain :

$$i\sigma \frac{d\tau}{dx} = i^2 r_l + \frac{d}{dx} \left(\kappa_l \frac{d\tau}{dx} \right),$$

which is equation 3 already obtained for the determination of the Thomson heat, thus checking our present account of the energy transformations.

We may now substitute in equation 17 the expression for $(\text{e.m.f.})_d$. In general $i = \left[(\text{e.m.f.})_d - \dfrac{dV}{dx}\right]\Big/ r_l$. Whence

$$i^2 r_l = i\left[(\text{e.m.f.})_d - \frac{\partial V}{\partial x}\right] = i\left[-\frac{d\tau}{dx}\int_0^\tau \frac{\sigma}{\tau}\,d\tau + f(\tau) - \frac{dV}{dx}\right].$$

On substituting back in 17, $i\dfrac{dV}{dx}$ and $i^2 r_l$ cancel, leaving

$$\frac{d}{dx}(iU) = i\left[\sigma\frac{d\tau}{dx} + \frac{d\tau}{dx}\int_0^\tau \frac{\sigma}{\tau}\,d\tau - f(\tau)\right].$$

But now the state of affairs is steady, so that $\dfrac{di}{dx} = 0$, and $\dfrac{d}{dx}(iU) = i\dfrac{dU}{dx}$. Furthermore

$$\sigma\frac{d\tau}{dx} + \frac{d\tau}{dx}\int_0^\tau \frac{\sigma}{\tau}\,d\tau \equiv \frac{d}{dx}\left[\tau\int_0^\tau \frac{\sigma}{\tau}\,d\tau\right],$$

as may be checked by direct differentiation. Hence:

$$\frac{dU}{dx} = \frac{d}{dx}\left[\tau\int_0^\tau \frac{\sigma}{\tau}\,d\tau\right] - f(\tau),$$

and

$$U = \tau\int_0^\tau \frac{\sigma}{\tau}\,d\tau - \int f(\tau)\,dx + U_0.$$

Now it is an obvious requirement that U shall be a function of temperature only. This demands that $f(\tau)$ vanish; if this were not the case we see that U would increase indefinitely as current flows along a uniform conductor all at the same temperature, which is absurd. The general relation is therefore:

$$U = \tau\int_0^\tau \frac{\sigma}{\tau}\,d\tau + U_0, \qquad\qquad \text{II, 18.}$$

where U_0 is independent of temperature, but, as far as this argument goes, may be a function of the orientation of the crystal rod.

It is to be noticed that this value for the convected energy is essentially different from that which would be given by the conventional description, which would set the convected energy equal to $\int_0^\tau \sigma \, d\tau$, treating the Thomson heat as the analog of the specific heat of ordinary matter. It is furthermore specially to be noted that if working e.m.f. and driving e.m.f. are set equal to each other, as is conventionally done, we would have obtained another expression for U consistent with neither. It may be verified in a moment that if we had put $i = \left[\sigma \dfrac{d\tau}{dx} - \dfrac{dV}{dx}\right] / r_l$, which comes from replacing $(e.m.f.)_d$ by $(e.m.f.)_w$, and substituted back in 17, we would have obtained $U = $ Const. This again is confirmation of the difficulties of the conventional description.

So far we have considered only what happens in the body of the crystal where there is a temperature gradient. Consider now the interface. The energy convected on opposite sides of the interface is, by the expression above, different, so that there must be an absorption of energy by the current at the interface. In fact, on flowing from $\parallel$ to $\perp$ we have:

(Energy absorbed at interface by unit quantity on flowing from $\parallel$ to $\perp$) =

$$\tau \int_0^\tau \frac{\sigma_\perp}{\tau} \, d\tau - \tau \int_0^\tau \frac{\sigma_\parallel}{\tau} \, d\tau + U_{0\perp} - U_{0\parallel}. \qquad \text{II, 19.}$$

Since there is no Poynting flow into the interface, this must be exactly equal to the Peltier heat flowing in at the interface. But $P_{\parallel\perp} = \tau \dfrac{dE_{\parallel\perp}}{d\tau}$ and this by equation 12 is exactly

$$\tau \int_0^\tau \frac{\sigma_\perp}{\tau} \, d\tau - \tau \int_0^\tau \frac{\sigma_\parallel}{\tau} \, d\tau.$$

Hence the energy requirements at the interface are exactly met if $U_{0\perp} = U_{0\parallel}$. That is, U_0 may be a function of the metal, but must be the same for all orientations in the crystal.

Unit current therefore convects with it energy

$$\tau \int_0^\tau \frac{\sigma}{\tau} \, d\tau + U_0.$$

The first part of this, omitting the term U_0 which is independent of temperature, must be formally described as thermal energy, which the current convects with it exactly as a stream of water convects thermal energy. The essential difference between the current of water and the electrical current is that the thermal energy convected by the electric current is a function of the metal in which it flows, as if the specific heat of a stream of water were dependent on the kind of pipe carrying it. In the body of the metal, in which current flows from one temperature to another, there is a transformation of this convected thermal energy to other forms, exactly as in a thermodynamic engine working between different temperatures. The electricity takes the rôle of the working fluid of an ordinary thermodynamic engine. The first law now demands that the difference between energy entering at the higher temperature and leaving at the lower temperature be equal to the amount transformed to other forms. This demand of the first law we have already seen to be satisfied. The second law demands that if the process is reversible, as we suppose it is, the amount of energy transformed be equal to the fraction $d\tau/\tau$ of the entering thermal energy. This demand may be shown at once to be satisfied. The energy transformed in an element of the body of the conductor of unit length is: $i\dfrac{dV}{dx}$, which flows out on the Poynting vector, plus the Joulean heat (which might have appeared as useful mechanical work instead of heat if a motor with proper back E.M.F. had been inserted in the element). Using the expression for the driving e.m.f. already given we get at once

$$i\frac{dV}{dx} + i^2 r_l = -\, i\frac{d\tau}{dx}\int_0^\tau \frac{\sigma\, d\tau}{\tau}.$$

This should be equal to the fraction $d\tau/\tau$ of the entering energy. For unit length $d\tau = \dfrac{d\tau}{dx}$. Substituting the value for the convected energy, the amount $-\dfrac{1}{\tau}\dfrac{d\tau}{dx}\left[\tau\int_0^\tau \dfrac{\sigma}{\tau}\, d\tau\right]$ should be transformed per unit current. (The negative sign comes from the fact that we have here to consider the energy entering at the higher temperature.) The two expressions are at once seen to be consistent, and our scheme of description is justified.

Thus far our argument has assumed a couple made of two branches of the same single crystal but with different orientations. We seek to extend to any isotropic material the description which is satisfactory for the crystal. We can make connection by way of the expression for the convected energy, $U = \tau \int_0^\tau \frac{\sigma}{\tau} d\tau + U_0$, in which the first term is thermal energy, and the second non-thermal, a function of the metal but not of temperature. We are bound to retain this expression for the convected energy for any metal; this is intuitively evident, or we can make an argument for it by starting with a fictitious non-cubic metal nearly like the actual isotropic (or cubic) metal, and continually decreasing the difference between the different orientations until in the limit we reach the cubic metal. Our expression for convected energy always holds for the crystal and must hold in the limit for the isotropic metal. It follows that when current flows across an interface between two different isotropic metals there is a difference of convected energy

$$U_B - U_A = \tau \left[\int \frac{\sigma_B - \sigma_A}{\tau} d\tau \right] + U_{0B} - U_{0A}$$

to be accounted for at the junction. The first term on the right-hand side is difference of thermal energy, and is equal to the Peltier heat flowing in at the interface. The second term $U_{0B} - U_{0A}$, is difference of non-thermal energy, and is accounted for by the Poynting flow from outside into the interface. $U_{0B} - U_{0A}$ is therefore the jump of electrostatic potential in passing across the interface between points in the interior of the two metals; it is a constructional quantity, and is not capable of direct measurement. It is not equal to the total Poynting flow into the region of the junction from outside space determined by the Volta potential difference, but is this flux diminished by the Poynting flux through the double layers along the surfaces of the metals A and B. We have not yet any way of knowing what the potential jumps are at the interface between metal and surrounding empty space, so that the difference $U_{0B} - U_{0A}$ is not yet uniquely connected with V_{AB}. If the two metals A and B are two orientations of the same crystal, however, the potential jump at the interface vanishes, and the double layers responsible for any Volta difference between two different orientations must be entirely situated on the free surfaces.

The expressions which we have derived for driving and working e.m.f. in crystals evidently carry over immediately to the general case, and we have for a unit element with a temperature gradient :

$$(\text{e.m.f.})_w = \sigma \operatorname{Grad} \tau. \hspace{3cm} \text{II, 20.}$$

$$(\text{e.m.f.})_d = - \operatorname{Grad} \tau \left[\int_0^\tau \frac{\sigma}{\tau} d\tau + f(\tau) \right]. \hspace{1cm} \text{II, 21.}$$

where $f(\tau)$ is some undetermined temperature function.

Finally, it is to be emphasized that the various quantities which we have introduced here, driving and working e.m.f.'s, convected energy, and potential jumps between points inside the metal, are purely constructional and not capable of direct measurement. But if we are going to admit constructional quantities at all, as we almost certainly must, and if we are going to demand of them that they satisfy thermodynamics and join on smoothly with directly measurable quantities, as we must if they are to be useful, it would seem that there is no stopping short of what we have done here. It is certainly a gratification that it is possible to find a set of constructional quantities which are internally consistent, and furthermore up to a certain point, unique. Those quantities which are uniquely determined we naturally think of as having physical reality, and we should, therefore, seek to so frame any detailed picture of the mechanism of electrical phenomena in a metal that these constructional quantities have their counterparts in distinct features of the mechanism.

CHAPTER III

THERMODYNAMIC ANALYSIS OF THE VOLTA EFFECT

Any phenomenon which involves reversible energy transformations may be made the subject of a thermodynamic analysis in which the first and second laws of thermodynamics are applied. Lorentz and later Lord Kelvin [5] independently made such an analysis of the Volta effect. The following argument gives essentially their results.

A parallel plate condenser is composed of two metals A and B; the distance of separation of the plates is small enough compared with the area so that edge effects may be neglected, and we may consider the energy changes per unit area of the plate. The plates are connected by a wire partly of A and partly of B, so that the junction between A and B is at some point in the wire. The Volta difference of potential is automatically set up between the plates, which thereby acquire a surface charge. The resulting electric field between the plates tends to draw them together, and this tendency must be resisted by the application of a force from outside. If the plates are allowed to draw together against this force, the system delivers mechanical work to the exterior. At the same time that the plates draw together charge must pass from one to the other through the connecting wire to maintain the Volta potential difference, and this motion of electricity constitutes a current which is capable of delivering energy to a suitable engine placed in the connecting wire. Conversely, by working this engine and charging the plates, they may be brought to any desired difference of potential. The whole system is furthermore to be maintained at constant temperature, and this temperature may be varied by proper heat interchange with the surroundings. As the variables specifying the state of the system we may take temperature, τ, distance of separation of the plates,

70

l, and surface charge per unit area on A, ρ, which varies when the potential difference varies and may conveniently replace the potential difference as an independent variable for purposes of analysis. The first law applied to the system now gives:

$$dQ = dU + dW. \qquad \text{III, 1.}$$

where dQ is heat absorbed by the system from the surroundings, dU change of internal energy, and dW work done by the system. We express dW in terms of the independent variables:

$$dW = \frac{\partial W}{\partial \tau} d\tau + \frac{\partial W}{\partial l} dl + \frac{\partial W}{\partial \rho} d\rho. \qquad \text{III, 2.}$$

Work is done only when the distance between the plates changes or current flows in the wire, so that $\dfrac{\partial W}{\partial \tau} = 0$. The mechanical force pulling the plates together is, per unit area, $2\pi\rho^2$, so that $\dfrac{\partial W}{\partial l} = -2\pi\rho^2$. The electric work done when current flows is the product of the quantity into the *effective* potential difference, which we have already seen to be $V - V_{BA}$, where V is the actual potential difference between the plates, measured between points immediately outside them, and is $4\pi\rho l$. Hence

$$\frac{\partial W}{\partial \rho} = -(4\pi\rho l - V_{BA}),$$

the minus sign resulting from the fact that the current delivers work when positive charge on A decreases.

We may also express dU as a function of the independent variables, writing:

$$dU = \frac{\partial U}{\partial \tau} d\tau + \frac{\partial U}{\partial l} dl + \frac{\partial U}{\partial \rho} d\rho. \qquad \text{III, 3.}$$

Substituting these various values now gives:

$$dQ = \frac{\partial U}{\partial \tau} d\tau + \left(-2\pi\rho^2 + \frac{\partial U}{\partial l}\right)dl + \left(V_{BA} - 4\pi\rho l + \frac{\partial U}{\partial \rho}\right)d\rho. \qquad \text{III, 4.}$$

This is the complete expression of the first law. The second law may now be applied in the form that dQ/τ is an exact differential. The condition that the differential be exact is that the cross derivatives of the coefficients of $d\tau$, dl, and $d\rho$ in the expression for dQ/τ shall be equal. There are three such coefficients and three conditions on the cross derivatives.

(1) The condition on the coefficients of $d\tau$ and dl is:

$$\frac{\partial}{\partial l}\left[\frac{1}{\tau}\frac{\partial U}{\partial \tau}\right] = \frac{\partial}{\partial \tau}\left[\frac{1}{\tau}\left(-2\pi\rho^2 + \frac{\partial U}{\partial l}\right)\right].$$

This gives, on expansion

$$\frac{1}{\tau}\frac{\partial^2 U}{\partial l\,\partial \tau} = \frac{1}{\tau}\frac{\partial^2 U}{\partial \tau\,\partial l} - \frac{1}{\tau^2}\left(-2\pi\rho^2 + \frac{\partial U}{\partial l}\right),$$

or

$$\frac{\partial U}{\partial l} = 2\pi\rho^2.$$

But

$$\frac{\partial U}{\partial l} = \frac{\partial Q}{\partial l} - \frac{\partial W}{\partial l},$$

and we have already found that

$$\frac{\partial W}{\partial l} = -2\pi\rho^2.$$

Hence this condition reduces to

$$\left(\frac{\partial Q}{\partial l}\right)_{\tau,\,\rho} = 0, \hspace{3cm} \text{III, 5.}$$

which states that no heat has to be absorbed to maintain the system isothermal if the distance between the plates is changed at constant surface charge. In other words, there are no heating effects connected with merely moving the plates back and forth. This, of course, is what we have all along assumed in electrostatics, but probably we never troubled to examine whether this was consistent with thermodynamics, or to find what was involved if it was consistent.

(2) The condition on the coefficients of dl and $d\rho$ is:

$$\frac{\partial}{\partial\rho}\left(-2\pi\rho^2 + \frac{\partial U}{\partial l}\right) = \frac{\partial}{\partial l}\left(V_{BA} - 4\pi\rho l + \frac{\partial U}{\partial\rho}\right).$$

Expanding,

$$\left(\frac{\partial V_{BA}}{\partial l}\right)_{\tau,\rho} = 0, \qquad\qquad \text{III, 6.}$$

or the Volta difference is not a function of the distance of separation of the plates as long as surface charge and temperature remain constant. This we have assumed, although the assumption has not appeared explicitly above.

(3) The condition on the coefficients of $d\tau$ and $d\rho$ is:

$$\frac{\partial}{\partial\rho}\left[\frac{1}{\tau}\frac{\partial U}{\partial\tau}\right] = \frac{\partial}{\partial\tau}\left[\frac{1}{\tau}\left(V_{BA} - 4\pi\rho l + \frac{\partial U}{\partial\rho}\right)\right].$$

Expanded, this gives

$$\frac{\partial V_{BA}}{\partial\tau} = \frac{1}{\tau}\left(V_{BA} - 4\pi\rho l + \frac{\partial U}{\partial\rho}\right).$$

Inspection of the original expression for dQ shows at once that the bracket on the right-hand side is $\dfrac{\partial Q}{\partial\rho}$, so that

$$\left(\frac{\partial V_{BA}}{\partial\tau}\right)_{l,\rho} = \frac{1}{\tau}\left(\frac{\partial Q}{\partial\rho}\right)_{\tau,l} \qquad\qquad \text{III, 7.}$$

This relation is essentially new; it was first obtained by Lorentz after making a correction in the original argument which was pointed out by Budde, and then later and independently by a superficially entirely different argument by Kelvin.

The temperature derivative of the Volta difference which appears on the left-hand side of 7 is a partial derivative, the distance between the plates and the density of surface charge being maintained constant. Experimentally, there would seem to be no evidence for a dependence of the Volta difference on ρ, but the possibility of such a dependence must be kept in mind. $\dfrac{\partial Q}{\partial\rho}$ on the right-hand side is the heat absorbed in order to maintain the system isothermal when the density of surface charge on A increases by unit amount, the distance between the plates being maintained constant. The surface charge on B decreases at the same time by unity, so that this involves the passage of a current through the wire connecting the plates, the direction of the current being from B to A. We know that such a current is accompanied by the ordinary Peltier heat at the junction of the two metals; it is therefore natural to identify the heat $\dfrac{\partial Q}{\partial \rho}$ with this Peltier heat, and this indeed is what Kelvin at first did, writing the equation as $\dfrac{dV_{BA}}{d\tau} = \dfrac{1}{\tau} P_{BA}$. Kelvin was led to identify $\dfrac{\partial Q}{\partial \rho}$ with P_{BA} all the more naturally because his express purpose in making an analysis of the Volta effect was to find some thermodynamic relation involving the parameters of the thermo-electric circuit by a method which should be free from the objection that irreversible processes were involved. It is to be emphasized that in the analysis above the system is always isothermal, so that no irreversible processes are involved, and the conclusions are thermodynamically rigorous. Apparently Kelvin was always bothered by the lack of rigor of his analysis for the thermo-electric circuit, and was constantly seeking to find some more rigorous line of argument. Kelvin then attempted to verify the equation experimentally, but the verification failed by a factor of more than a thousandfold. From this Kelvin drew the conclusion, as he had in a corresponding situation with respect to the thermo-electric circuit, that there must be some as yet unknown thermal phenomenon involved. He therefore postulated the existence of a reversible heating effect in the surface of a conductor when charge is added to or subtracted from it. This should be an effect per unit area, and should be linear in the charge, changing sign when the sign of the charge changes. The reason that just this effect was postulated is that it seems to be the only conceivable one that meets all the requirements. There may, of course, be other heating effects. Thus there is certainly an effect due to the stresses set up in the material of the conductor resisting the tendency of the charge to leave the surface, but this effect will be proportional to the square of the charge, and may be made vanishingly small in comparison with the other. Then there may conceivably be transient effects while the current is building up to a steady state, but such effects have not the right dimensions, and may be made to vanish by making the changes sufficiently slowly. There is also a Joulean development of heat as charge spreads over the surface, but this is irreversible, is not linear in the charge, and again may be made to vanish by making the changes sufficiently slowly.

The necessity of assuming just such a new surface heating effect as did Kelvin was also recognized by Lorentz after his attention had been called to it by Budde. Lorentz's analysis yielded the same result as the analysis of Kelvin, or the analysis above, which is formally different from either.

Granting now the existence of the " surface heat of charging " as Tonks and Langmuir [6] have called it, the thermodynamic relation becomes:

$$\frac{\partial V_{AB}}{\partial \tau} = \frac{1}{\tau} P'_{AB}, \qquad \text{III, 8.}$$

where P' is not the ordinary Peltier heat but includes both ordinary Peltier heat and the new surface heat of charging. Let us call the heat of charging P_{AS} and P_{BS} for metals A and B. Then since passage of positive current from A to B means a decrease of the surface charge on A, we evidently have

$$P'_{AB} = P_{AB} - P_{AS} + P_{BS} \qquad \text{III, 9.}$$

and

$$\frac{\partial V_{AB}}{d\tau} = \frac{1}{\tau} (P_{AB} - P_{AS} + P_{BS}). \qquad \text{III, 10.}$$

Kelvin's attempted experimental evaluation of $\dfrac{\partial V_{AB}}{\partial \tau}$ in order to compare with the Peltier heat was, of course, made under extremely unfavorable conditions, and his failure to verify the relation can be given no significance whatever. The experiment is evidently one requiring all the extreme refinements of modern high vacuum technique, and I gather from those conversant with such matters that it is doubtful whether the technique is even yet good enough to permit a direct determination of $\dfrac{\partial V}{\partial \tau}$ which would give a reproducible result, truly characteristic of the metal. So far as I know, the best evaluation of $\dfrac{\partial V}{\partial \tau}$ has brought Kelvin's factor of discrepancy of 1000 down to about 50. If one assumes that this factor 50 is genuine, one can calculate an upper limit for the magnitude of the surface heat. The numerical magnitude thus obtained shows that it would be of almost prohibitive experimental difficulty to attempt to detect directly the surface heat from a change of temperature of a surface receiving a charge. The difficulty is that any change of temperature of the surface is immediately swallowed by the inert mass of metal back of the surface, and if one seeks to reduce by a suitable amount the inert mass of metal, the electrostriction effects become correspondingly large. Perhaps it might be possible to eliminate the electrostriction effects because they are proportional to the square of the charge. But probably the best way of establishing the existence of the effect is by so improving vacuum technique as to give a good value for $\dfrac{\partial V}{\partial \tau}$.

In spite of the experimental difficulty of measuring the effect, it is of extreme importance in theoretical thermodynamic analysis, and, as we shall see, occurs also in the phenomena of thermionic emission. It must not be disregarded, as very large differences may thereby be introduced in the relations deduced. Such a surface heat is not inconsistent with the most recent views as to the nature of the electronic structure of metals, which would suggest that the binding forces on the electrons are different on the surface and in the interior, so that the characteristic frequency would be different on the surface and in the interior, and so the upper available level of the degenerate Fermi gas.

The relations just found are essentially all that can be got by thermodynamics; other relations may of course be found, but they involve only formal transformations. Our relations have involved certain quantities, principally V and $\dfrac{\partial V}{\partial \tau}$, which must be determined by experiment, and about which thermodynamics has nothing to say. Before dismissing the problem finally it is interesting to inquire what is the complete list of independent quantities which must be determined by experiment in order to completely characterize the thermal behavior of the system. Thermodynamically the behavior of the system in any small neighborhood is completely determined if we know the six coefficients $\frac{\partial W}{\partial \tau}$, $\frac{\partial W}{\partial l}$, $\frac{\partial W}{\partial \rho}$, $\frac{\partial Q}{\partial \tau}$, $\frac{\partial Q}{\partial l}$, and $\frac{\partial Q}{\partial \rho}$. The three derivatives of W are determined by the mechanics of the system and have been written down. V_{BA} is involved in these derivatives. Of the Q derivatives, we have shown that $\frac{\partial Q}{\partial l} = 0$, and have found $\frac{\partial Q}{\partial \rho}$. There remains only $\frac{\partial Q}{\partial \tau}$, a specific heat, which must be determined by experiment and about which thermodynamics can say nothing. This specific heat is in general a function of τ, l, and ρ, and the dependence on any of these parameters is thermodynamically undetermined. In particular, if it depends on ρ, there is a contribution to the specific heat made by the surface charge, which means that the surface charge has a specific heat different from the neutral metal. This must be determined by experiment; we shall see later in discussing thermionic emission that there are reasons for thinking that the specific heat of the surface charge must be nearly the same as that of the metal.

It is interesting to notice that the mathematical assumptions which we have made about the form of the heating effects impose definite restrictions on any physical picture which is permissible to represent the phenomena. We have assumed the surface heat to be linear in the surface charge; this means that the heating effect when one electron is added to the surface is the negative of that when one electron is subtracted. The physical picture must therefore in some way achieve symmetry with regard to the addition and subtraction of electrons. The most natural picture perhaps is to think of the positive surface charge in the form of positive ions in the surface, and the negative surface charge in the form of electrons miscellaneously added to the surface. But this picture does not have the requisite symmetry. If the positive charge is to be thought of as due to the presence of additional positive ions in the surface, then the negative charge must be also thought of as due to negative *ions* in the surface, that is, each electron added to the surface must attach itself to some definite surface atom. Another way of achieving the necessary symmetry is to think of the free electrons in the interior of the metal, which are perhaps something like a jelly in which the positive ions are embedded, as extending right up to the surface; positive surface charge then means the subtraction of an electron from this jelly, and negative surface charge the addition of an electron to it.

CHAPTER IV

THERMIONIC PHENOMENA

It is established by experiment that negative electricity is spontaneously emitted from a heated metal; if the metal is isolated in an indefinitely large empty space, the emission proceeds until the accumulation of positive charge on the surface prevents, by static attraction, the emission of further negative charge. If the metal is not isolated, but attached to a source of negative electricity, such as a battery, the emission goes on indefinitely. The process is analogous in many respects to ordinary evaporation, with the complication that the vapor is charged and so is subject to electrostatic forces in addition to the gas pressure in an ordinary vapor. The emission of electricity is a very strong function of temperature; in regions where it is capable of measurement formulas have been found which successfully reproduce the emission over a range of perhaps 10^8 fold. These formulas demand some emission at all temperatures, so that in theoretical discussions such emission is accordingly considered at every temperature, although it may be far below any possibility of experimental detection at present.

Every metal, therefore, is to be pictured as surrounded by an atmosphere of negative electricity when in a state of complete equilibrium. The existence of this atmosphere can be detected by suitable probes at high enough temperatures. We always go further, however, and picture this surrounding atmosphere as made up of electrons just as we picture an ordinary vapor as made up of gas molecules. It must be recognized that we are here dealing with a construction, but it is one which has proved so extremely useful everywhere, just as have the molecules of kinetic gas theory, that no physicist will hesitate very much to accept this construction as real, or to think of the electrical atmosphere surrounding a metal as a mon-atomic gas of electrons.

An electrical gas composed of electrons will exert an ordinary

79

gas pressure in virtue of the momentum which the electrons have because of temperature agitation. The mechanism by which the momentum gets transferred to the walls of the vessel is doubtless electrical in character, just as the rebound of two electrons in collision is brought about by the force of electrostatic repulsion. The pressure forces are, however, only called into play by the proximity of the electron itself and do not correspond to a large-scale, smooth electrical field of force which can be included in the Maxwell equations. This is the sort of thing that we have already come across; the collisional or pressure forces are, from this point of view, to be described as "non-electrostatic." In addition to the pressure forces an electron gas experiences other forces properly to be described as electrostatic, due to the average potential of its own distributed charge. An electron finds itself on the average in the midst of a similarly charged electrical jelly. The force on each electron doubles if the average density of the jelly doubles (that is, if the electron gas density doubles). Furthermore, the number of electrons acted on doubles when the density doubles. It follows that the contribution to the pressure on the walls arising from this electrostatic (or body charge) effect increases as the square of the density, whereas the ordinary gas pressure increases as the first power. Hence the electrostatic gas pressure may be made vanishingly small in comparison with the ordinary gas pressure by going to small densities. Furthermore, the total amount of gas present is a factor in determining the ratio between ordinary gas pressure and electrostatic gas pressure. This may be seen qualitatively by considering that the electrostatic force at the surface of a sphere of constant density varies directly as the radius of the sphere. The ratio of electrostatic gas pressure to ordinary gas pressure is therefore smaller in vessels of smaller size. This whole matter has been considered quantitatively by von Laue,[7] who has shown that in the range of conditions corresponding to laboratory practice it is justifiable to neglect the electrostatic forces, and treat the electron vapor in equilibrium with ordinary metals as an ordinary perfect mon-atomic gas of neutral atoms.

We may now apply thermodynamics to the evaporation of electrons from a metal exactly as we may apply it to the evapora-

tion of ordinary substances. Imagine a metal at the bottom of
a cylindrical box covered with a freely moving piston, the whole
system to be maintained at constant temperature. The piston
is originally in contact with the metal, so that the volume of the
vapor phase is zero. We now withdraw the piston so slowly that
the equilibrium vapor pressure is continuously maintained.
During this process the piston receives mechanical work determined by the vapor pressure, and heat flows into the system in
order to maintain it isothermal. The relations are exactly the
same as in the evaporation of an ordinary substance, and the
same thermodynamics applies. In particular, Clapeyron's equation applies which gives the dependence of vapor pressure on
temperature, or :

$$\frac{d\tau}{dp} = \frac{\tau \Delta v}{L},$$

where Δv is the change of volume of the system when one gm mol
(or any definite quantity) of the solid evaporates, and L is the
latent heat of evaporation of one gm mol (or of the same definite
quantity), under the conditions just specified, that is, in an
isolated system.

This equation is exact; it involves no assumption as to the
nature of the substances, nor is any assumption involved as to
whether the system obeys the classical or the quantum statistics.
To get further, we may approximate by applying the perfect gas
law to the electron gas, neglecting the volume of the solid in
comparison with that of the vapor, which amounts to setting
Δv equal to the volume of the gas. This approximation can
introduce no appreciable error when one considers that at room
temperature the electron gas pressure is so low that in the electron
vapor in equilibrium with tungsten, for example, there is only
one electron in a sphere of 350 light years radius. For gases of
such densities quantum mechanics shows that the perfect gas
law is an entirely adequate approximation. For such a gas we
have, therefore, $p = n\kappa\tau$, where n is the number of molecules of
gas (here electrons) per cm³, and κ is the gas constant per molecule,
or 1.35×10^{-16}. Differentiation of the gas equation now gives

$$dp = \kappa(\tau \, dn + n \, d\tau).$$

Substitute this in Clapeyron's equation, and also replace Δv by v, obtaining:

$$d\tau = \tau \frac{v}{L} \kappa (\tau\, dn + n\, d\tau)$$

$$= \frac{\kappa\tau^2}{\underset{nv}{\underline{L}}} \left(\frac{dn}{n} + \frac{d\tau}{\tau} \right).$$

But $\dfrac{L}{nv}$ is obviously the latent heat per electron. Denote this by η, and rearrange the equation, getting:

$$\frac{\eta}{\kappa\tau^2}\, d\tau = \frac{dn}{n} + \frac{d\tau}{\tau}.$$

Integration gives at once

$$\int \frac{\eta}{\kappa\tau^2}\, d\tau = \log n + \log \tau + \log \text{Const},$$

or, $$n = C\tau^{-1}\, \epsilon^{\int_{\tau_0}^{\tau} \frac{\eta}{\kappa\tau^2} d\tau}, \qquad\qquad \text{IV, 1.}$$

in which C is not a function of temperature but may, as far as this argument goes, be a function of the metal, because $C = n_0\tau_0$, where τ_0 is arbitrary. We evidently cannot put $\tau_0 = 0$ in this expression because of mathematical difficulty with the convergence of the integral.

Now apply equation 1 to the electron vapor which surrounds two metals which constitute a Volta condenser. If the system is maintained isothermal, it must come to equilibrium. The density of the electron vapor immediately outside each metal is given by the equation. But in the space surrounding the metals the Volta difference of potential is spontaneously maintained. This gives rise to an electric force in the electron gas, which in general would produce a migration from the weaker to the stronger parts of the field until a pressure gradient is built up to counteract this field. Equilibrium demands that the pressure gradient necessary to equilibrate the Volta potential difference be exactly the same as that produced spontaneously by the evaporation of electrons at the surfaces of the two metals. The equation of equilibrium in the electron gas is obviously

$$dp = e\mathcal{E}n\,dx = e\mathcal{E}\frac{p}{\kappa\tau}\,dx.$$

e is the charge of the electron, and is taken as intrinsically negative, -4.7×10^{-10} E.S.U.

Integration gives:

$$\log\frac{p_B}{p_A} = \frac{e}{\kappa\tau}\int\mathcal{E}\,dx = -\frac{e}{\kappa\tau}\int\frac{\partial V}{\partial x}\,dx = -\frac{e}{\kappa\tau}(V_B - V_A) = -\frac{e}{\kappa\tau}V_{AB},$$

or, since p is proportional to n,

$$\frac{n_A}{n_B} = \epsilon^{\frac{eV_{AB}}{\kappa\tau}}, \qquad\qquad \text{IV, 2.}$$

or,

$$V_{AB} = \frac{\kappa\tau}{e}\log\frac{n_A}{n_B}. \qquad\qquad \text{IV, 3.}$$

It is interesting to notice parenthetically that this expression gives the means of splitting V_{AB} into two terms depending only on the respective metals, which we have already seen to be demanded by the Volta law of tensions. This is obvious, for

$$V_{AB} = \frac{\kappa\tau}{e}\log n_A - \frac{\kappa\tau}{e}\log n_B.$$

We may evidently add to both terms any universal temperature function.

Equation 1, applied to each metal, now gives

$$\frac{n_A}{n_B} = \frac{C_A}{C_B}\epsilon^{\int_{\tau_0}^{\tau}\frac{\eta_A - \eta_B}{\kappa\tau^2}\,d\tau}, \qquad\qquad \text{IV, 4.}$$

or eliminating n_A/n_B between equations 3 and 4,

$$\frac{e}{\kappa\tau}V_{AB} = \log C_A - \log C_B + \int_{\tau_0}^{\tau}\frac{\eta_A - \eta_B}{\kappa\tau^2}\,d\tau. \qquad \text{IV, 5.}$$

But C_A and C_B are independent of temperature and may therefore be eliminated by differentiating with respect to τ, giving, after a simple reduction,

$$\eta_A - \eta_B = - eV_{AB} + e\tau \frac{dV_{AB}}{d\tau}, \qquad \text{IV, 6.}$$

a relation between the latent heats of evaporation and the Volta potential difference.

The "latent heat of evaporation" of electrons has been measured experimentally and may be found in the literature. The method is to measure the additional heat input, in the form of Joulean heating against resistance, required to maintain a metal isothermal when the emitted electrons are continually drawn off by an applied external field, in excess of that required to maintain the wire at the same temperature but with no electron emission.

It would appear at first sight therefore as if we could obtain $\dfrac{dV}{d\tau}$ from equation 6 in terms of the measured values of the latent heat, and so obtain an estimate of the "surface heat of charging" discussed in the last chapter. It is especially to be emphasized, however, that the latent heat measured by the method just outlined is not the same as the latent heat in equation 6 above. The η above is the latent heat in the isolated system in which a positive charge builds up on the surface as the electron vapor is formed. When the latent heat is measured experimentally, however, a fresh supply of electrons is continually being fed into the metal to replace those which evaporate, so that the surface charge is maintained constant. To distinguish this experimentally measured latent heat from that above we write η_ρ, and call it the latent heat at constant surface charge. We may use an additional subscript to denote the metal when necessary. There is an obvious relation between the two surface heats and the surface heat of charging, namely:

$$\eta = \eta_\rho - eP_S. \qquad \text{IV, 7.}$$

We may now obtain another relation involving the heats of evaporation by a simple cyclic process. Given the two metals A and B, as shown in Figure 12, at constant temperature. They are surrounded by chambers, connected by a tube as shown, with insulating walls, in which the electron vapor comes to its equilibrium density. At the surface of each metal the densities are as already given. The surface of each metal is also all at constant potential, the difference between the two being V_{AB}. In the region connecting the two enclosures there is a potential drop of amount V_{AB}, and a pressure gradient in the electron gas to balance the resulting electric field.

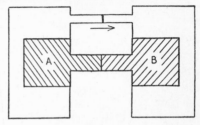

Fig. 12

Imagine a piston in the connecting pipe. This is electrically neutral and is exposed to the same pressure on the two sides. Now displace this piston toward B so slowly that the system is always in equilibrium. The result of the motion of the piston is to condense electrons into B, move them through the metal across the interface B–A, evaporate them from A, and transfer them in the vapor phase from the surface of A to the surface of B. The process is isothermal and reversible, and hence no work is done and no heat absorbed. Obviously the piston does no work, the pressure on its two sides always being the same. We write down the condition that no net heat be absorbed. Heat is absorbed in four places: at the two metal surfaces where evaporation or condensation takes place, at the metal interface, and in the body of the gas. The heats of vaporization are obviously the heats at constant surface charge. The heat at the interface is the ordinary Peltier heat P_{BA}. Call the heat absorbed by the gas per electron transferred Q. Then the condition of no net heat absorption is:

$$\eta_{\rho A} - \eta_{\rho B} + eP_{BA} + Q = 0. \qquad \text{IV, 8.}$$

The heat Q absorbed by the vapor requires special consideration. The problem is evidently the exact analog of a rising current of air in the earth's gravitational field. It is well known that there is a cooling effect under these conditions, so that heat inflow would be necessary to maintain the rising air isothermal. The first law of thermodynamics applied to the rising gas demands that the initial internal energy plus the energy received during the rise be equal to the final internal energy. But in a perfect gas at constant temperature the internal energy is independent

FIG. 13

of volume. Therefore, since there is no change of internal energy, the total energy received during the rise must vanish. The energy so received is of three sorts: pressure work across the boundaries, work against gravitation (or in our case against the electric field), and heat. The pressure work received across the boundaries vanishes, as may be seen by an inspection of Figure 13. For the total pressure work is that received by the lower surface on rising from A to C minus that done by the upper surface in rising from B to D. For positions of the upper and lower surfaces between B and C the work received by one surface in any displacement, as indicated by the dotted lines, is nullified by that done by the other surface during the same displacement. The total is therefore the difference between that received by the lower surface in moving from A to B and that done by the upper in moving from C to D. But these two are equal, since for an isothermal gas $p_1 v_1 = p_2 v_2$. The total pressure work is therefore zero, and the net work done against the gravitational (or electric) field must be provided by the heat input. This gives at once, applied to our cycle above, $Q = eV_{AB}$, and equation 8 reduces to

$$\eta_{\rho A} - \eta_{\rho B} = e\,(P_{AB} - V_{AB}), \qquad\qquad \text{IV, 9.}$$

an equation involving only quantities directly measurable, and furthermore of such magnitudes that they have actually been determined. I am not aware that the equation has been checked, however, by measurements all made under the same conditions.

We may replace η_ρ in this equation by its equivalent $\eta + eP_S$ (according to equation 7), and then eliminate $\eta_A - \eta_B$ between the equation thus obtained and equation 6, obtaining:

$$\tau \frac{dV_{AB}}{d\tau} = P_{AB} - P_{AS} + P_{BS}. \qquad\qquad \text{IV, 10.}$$

This is the same as equation III, 10; we have here obtained it by an entirely independent method, and have thus checked the consistency of our analysis.

It is to be noticed that if we had identified η_ρ with η, we would have obtained immediately on combining 9 with 6, $\tau \dfrac{dV_{AB}}{d\tau} = P_{AB}$, which is the same as 10, in which the surface heats have been set equal to zero. But neglecting the surface heats is exactly equivalent to setting $\eta_\rho = \eta$, as we see at once from equation 7. If the surface heats do vanish, then since for the thermo-electric circuit $\dfrac{dE_{AB}}{d\tau} = \dfrac{1}{\tau} P_{AB}$, we would have $\dfrac{dV_{AB}}{d\tau} = \dfrac{dE_{AB}}{d\tau}$. This equation may be found in various places in the literature; it can be correct only if the effect of the surface heats vanishes. There is no experimental evidence for the correctness of this equation, the error in $\dfrac{dV_{AB}}{d\tau}$ being high, so that we get no hold on the surface heats by this method.

Additional relations may now be obtained connecting the heats of vaporization with the Thomson heat of the ordinary thermo-electric circuit. Solve equation 9 for V_{AB} and differentiate with respect to temperature, obtaining:

$$\frac{dV_{AB}}{d\tau} = \frac{1}{e}\left(\frac{d\eta_{\rho B}}{d\tau} - \frac{d\eta_{\rho A}}{d\tau}\right) + \frac{dP_{AB}}{d\tau} \qquad \text{IV, 11.}$$

$$= \frac{1}{\tau}[P_{AB} - P_{AS} + P_{BS}]$$

by equation 10.

But the equations of the thermo-electric circuit give

$$\frac{1}{\tau} P_{AB} = \frac{dE_{AB}}{d\tau}, \text{ and } \frac{dP_{AB}}{d\tau} = \frac{dE_{AB}}{d\tau} + \sigma_B - \sigma_A.$$

Substituting,

$$\frac{d\eta_{\rho A}}{d_\tau} + e\left(\sigma_A - \frac{1}{\tau} P_{AS}\right) = \frac{d\eta_{\rho B}}{d\tau} + e\left(\sigma_B - \frac{1}{\tau} P_{BS}\right) \quad \text{IV, 12.}$$

or,

$$\frac{d\eta_\rho}{d\tau} + e\left(\sigma - \frac{1}{\tau} P_S\right) \qquad \text{IV, 13.}$$

is the same for all metals, and therefore must be a universal temperature function.

The universal value of 13 may now be derived by an argument similar to one used by Richardson. Given a dumb-bell-shaped piece of metal, as shown in Figure 14, with the two ends maintained at a temperature difference $\Delta\tau$. Each end is surrounded

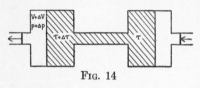

Fig. 14

by a chamber into which evaporation of electrons takes place until the equilibrium pressure at each temperature is reached. There will also be a characteristic difference of electrostatic potential between the vapors immediately over the metals at the two ends. Now push a piston into the chamber at the lower temperature, condensing into the metal a certain number of electrons, and simultaneously withdraw a piston from the chamber at higher temperature, evaporating the same number of electrons from the hot end. The system is now transferred to its initial condition by expanding the transferred electrons from $p + \Delta p$ and $\tau + \Delta\tau$ back to p and τ at the potential $V + \Delta V$ characteristic of the upper temperature, and then moving this electron gas bodily at constant p and τ back from $V + \Delta V$ to V, where it may be incorporated into the chamber at lower temperature with no additional mechanical or thermal effects. The condensation and evaporation are accompanied by heat of evaporation, which is evidently the heat at constant surface charge, η_ρ. We neglect the irreversible transfer of heat by conduction through the metal during this process, just as we did for the thermo-electric circuit, and set the total change of entropy in the process equal to zero, since the system has been restored to its initial condition. The total change of entropy for unit quantity of electricity transferred gives the equation :

$$-\frac{1}{e}\frac{\eta_\rho}{\tau} + \frac{\sigma\,\Delta\tau}{\tau} + \frac{1}{e}\frac{\eta_\rho + \Delta\tau\,\dfrac{d\eta_\rho}{d\tau}}{\tau + \Delta\tau} + \frac{1}{e}\Delta S = 0, \quad \text{IV, 14}$$

where ΔS is the entropy change per electron of the electron gas. The process of transfer from $V + \Delta V$ to V is evidently without change of entropy, because only mechanical forces are here involved, just as lifting a closed box of gas at constant temperature through the earth's gravitational field involves no change of entropy. We have then,

$$\Delta S = - \left(\frac{\partial S}{\partial \tau}\right)_p \Delta \tau - \left(\frac{\partial S}{\partial p}\right)_\tau \Delta p.$$

In general, for any substance,

$$\left(\frac{\partial S}{\partial \tau}\right)_p = \frac{C_p}{\tau}, \text{ and } \left(\frac{\partial S}{\partial p}\right)_\tau = - \left(\frac{\partial v}{\partial \tau}\right)_p.$$

But the electron vapor satisfies the perfect gas laws, and hence

$$C_p = \frac{\gamma}{\gamma - 1} \kappa,$$

where γ is the ratio of the specific heats, $\frac{5}{3}$ for a mon-atomic gas, and $\left(\frac{\partial v}{\partial \tau}\right)_p = \frac{\kappa}{p}.$

Hence

$$\Delta S = - \frac{\gamma\kappa}{\gamma - 1}\frac{\Delta \tau}{\tau} + \frac{\kappa}{p}\Delta p.$$

Substituting above gives:

$$\frac{1}{e}\frac{d}{d\tau}\left(\frac{\eta_\rho}{\tau}\right) + \frac{\sigma}{\tau} + \frac{1}{e}\left[\frac{-\gamma\kappa}{\tau\,(\gamma - 1)} + \frac{\kappa}{p}\frac{dp}{d\tau}\right] = 0.$$

But we have already found

$$\frac{\eta}{\kappa\tau^2} d\tau = \frac{\eta_\rho - eP_S}{\kappa\tau^2} d\tau = \frac{dn}{n} + \frac{d\tau}{\tau} = \frac{dp}{p}.$$

Substitution gives at once

$$\frac{d\eta_\rho}{d\tau} + e\left(\sigma - \frac{P_S}{\tau}\right) = \frac{\gamma\kappa}{\gamma - 1}. \qquad \text{IV, 15.}$$

This is the desired universal function, which thus appears not only independent of the metal, but also independent of temperature.

Additional information may be obtained by applying the first law to the cycle just described, putting the total heat absorbed equal to the total work done. Work is done in the manipulation of the pistons and in the transfer of gas from $V + \Delta V$ to V. Heat is absorbed during evaporation and condensation, transfer of the electricity through the unequally heated metal, and expansion of the gas from $p + \Delta p$, $\tau + \Delta \tau$ to p, τ.

The work done per electron is:

$$(pv)_{\tau + \Delta \tau} - (pv)_\tau - \left(\frac{\partial W}{\partial \tau}\right)_p \Delta \tau - \left(\frac{\partial W}{\partial p}\right)_\tau \Delta p + e \, \Delta V.$$

The heat absorbed per electron is:

$$\frac{d\eta_\rho}{d\tau} + e\sigma \, \Delta \tau - \left(\frac{\partial Q}{\partial \tau}\right)_p \Delta \tau - \left(\frac{\partial Q}{\partial p}\right)_\tau \Delta p.$$

In general:

$$\left(\frac{\partial W}{\partial \tau}\right)_p = p \left(\frac{\partial v}{\partial \tau}\right)_p, \quad \left(\frac{\partial W}{\partial p}\right)_\tau = p \left(\frac{\partial v}{\partial p}\right)_\tau$$

$$\left(\frac{\partial Q}{\partial \tau}\right)_p = C_p, \quad \left(\frac{\partial Q}{\partial p}\right)_\tau = - \tau \left(\frac{\partial v}{\partial \tau}\right)_p,$$

and in particular, for a perfect gas:

$$\left(\frac{\partial W}{\partial \tau}\right)_p = \kappa, \quad \left(\frac{\partial W}{\partial p}\right)_\tau = - \frac{\kappa\tau}{p}.$$

$$\left(\frac{\partial Q}{\partial \tau}\right)_p = \frac{\gamma}{\gamma - 1} \kappa, \quad \left(\frac{\partial Q}{\partial p}\right)_\tau = - \frac{\kappa\tau}{p}.$$

Substitution gives at once

$$\frac{d\eta_\rho}{d\tau} + e\sigma - \frac{\gamma\kappa}{\gamma - 1} = e \frac{dV}{d\tau}. \qquad\qquad \text{IV, 16.}$$

Combining with equation 15 gives

$$\frac{dV}{d\tau} = \frac{P_S}{\tau}. \qquad\qquad \text{IV, 17.}$$

This equation was also obtained by Lorentz by an entirely different method, so that again we have presumptive evidence of the correctness of the analysis.

The meaning of the $\frac{dV}{d\tau}$ of this equation is to be carefully noticed; it is the difference of potential which is automatically set up between points at unit difference of temperature immediately outside an unequally heated metal, *free circulation of the electrons through the vapor being prevented.* It is the Volta difference of potential which would be observed between two plates of the same metal at different temperatures, the absolute temperature being so low that spontaneous emission of electrons from the metal is negligible. It is a quantity which should be capable of measurement at ordinary temperatures. We have here therefore a possible experimental method of determining the surface heat. It is not evident, however, that experimentally it would be easier to obtain reproducible values of $\frac{dV}{d\tau}$ between plates of the same metal at different temperatures than to obtain reproducible values for $\frac{dV_{AB}}{d\tau}$. A determination of $\frac{dV}{d\tau}$ offers the advantage, however, that it gives directly the surface heat of the single metal involved, instead of the difference of two surface heats, as does $\frac{dV_{AB}}{d\tau}$.

The Volta difference of potential set up between two plates of the same metal at different temperatures would not be expected in general to be such that the electron atmosphere in the space between the plates would be in equilibrium at the pressures automatically generated by the evaporation from the two surfaces. Failure of such equilibrium would result in a continuous circulation of electrons across the intervening space and back through the solid metal. Such a circulation would be maintained at the expense of heat conveyed by the circulation between the two reservoirs which maintain the two plates at different temperatures. Such a circulation is actually observed in the case of many metals; it may obviously be described in other words as a spontaneous thermionic emission of electrons between a hot and cold specimen of the same metal.   If there were no such spontaneous circulation, a pressure gradient in the electron vapor would be required of

$$\frac{\Delta p}{p} = - e \frac{\Delta V}{\kappa \tau}.$$

But

$$\frac{\Delta p}{p} = \frac{\eta}{\kappa \tau^2} \Delta \tau = \frac{\eta_\rho - e P_S}{\kappa \tau^2} \Delta \tau.$$

This, combined with $\dfrac{\Delta V}{\Delta \tau} = \dfrac{P_S}{\tau}$ would demand that $\eta_\rho = 0$.   But η_ρ is capable of direct experimental measurement, and is certainly not zero.   This confirms the experimental observation of spontaneous thermionic emission between different pieces of the same metal at different temperatures, and means that P_S cannot be zero.

We have here therefore obtained positive evidence of the reality of a surface heat not identically zero, so that this quantity must be scrupulously retained in any thermodynamic analysis.

Thus far in the analysis of this chapter we have dealt only with quantities which in principle are capable of direct measurement; this is obviously true of most of the quantities, which have actually been measured.   The difficulty with the surface heat is not one of principle, but is one of numerical magnitude.   Similarly in principle we might explore the space surrounding a metal and by drawing off the electron vapor actually determine the density of space charge, and so the n_A of our analysis.   It is now of interest to go a little further, and introduce some of the constructional quantities which we have already considered in previous chapters.   Consider in the first place the electric potential in the body of the metal and the jumps in this potential at the various interfaces.   Call the jump in potential between the metal A and surrounding empty space S_{AE} and the potential gradient inside the metal spontaneously set up on open circuit σ''_A.   At temperatures so low that there is no spontaneous emission of electrons from the metal let the system come to electrical equilibrium on open circuit with the two ends of the metal at a difference of temperature $\Delta \tau$.   The total change of electrostatic potential in describing a complete circuit, into the metal at one end, through the metal, out at the other end, and back to the starting point through empty space, must be zero. This gives at once:

$$- S_{AE} + \sigma''_A \, \Delta\tau + \left(S_{AE} + \Delta\tau \, \frac{dS_{AE}}{d\tau} \right) - \Delta V = 0.$$

Whence

$$\frac{dS_{AE}}{d\tau} + \sigma''_A - \frac{dV_A}{d\tau} = 0,$$

or, replacing $\frac{dV}{d\tau}$ by $\frac{P_S}{\tau}$,

$$\frac{dS_E}{d\tau} + \sigma'' - \frac{P_S}{\tau} = 0 \qquad \text{IV, 18.}$$

for every metal. The σ'' is obviously what we have previously called the (e.m.f.)$_d$ in the unequally heated metal, as is seen at once on setting $i = 0$ in the general relation I, 4. But we have already found the value of (e.m.f.)$_d$, so that

$$\sigma'' = - \int_0^\tau \frac{\sigma}{\tau} \, d\tau + f(\tau). \qquad \text{IV, 19.}$$

Combination of equation 18 above for $\frac{dS_E}{d\tau}$ with equation 15 previously found for $\frac{d\eta_\rho}{d\tau}$ gives:

$$\frac{d}{d\tau} \left(\eta_\rho - e S_E \right) + e \left[\sigma + \int_0^\tau \frac{\sigma}{\tau} \, d\tau - f(\tau) \right] = \frac{\gamma\kappa}{\gamma - 1}, \quad \text{IV, 20.}$$

an equation by which the temperature derivative of the constructional quantity S_E is determined, except for the universal temperature function, in terms of measurable quantities.

It appears therefore that although the absolute value of the jump of potential at the surface of a metal is not determined by thermodynamics its temperature derivative is nevertheless fixed, except for a universal temperature function. If the relative values of the surface jumps for any two metals are given at 0° Abs, their relative values at all other temperatures are fixed in terms of observational quantities.

The temperature variation of the potential jump at an interface between two metals is now also determined. Calling S_{BA} the potential jump on crossing the interface from B to A, we have in general

$$S_{EB} + S_{BA} + S_{AE} + V_{AB} = 0. \qquad \text{IV, 21.}$$

Whence

$$\frac{dS_{AB}}{d\tau} = \frac{dV_{AB}}{d\tau} + \frac{dS_{AE}}{d\tau} - \frac{dS_{BE}}{d\tau}.$$

But from equation 20,

$$\frac{d}{d\tau}(S_{AE} - S_{BE}) = \sigma_A - \sigma_B + \int_0^\tau \frac{\sigma_A - \sigma_B}{\tau}\, d\tau + \frac{1}{e}\frac{d}{d\tau}[\eta_{\rho A} - \eta_{\rho B}].$$

Also

$$\frac{dV_{AB}}{d\tau} = \frac{1}{\tau}[P_{AB} - P_{AS} + P_{AS}]$$

and

$$\frac{d}{d\tau}[\eta_{\rho A} - \eta_{\rho B}] = e\left[\sigma_B - \sigma_A - \frac{P_{BS} - P_{AS}}{\tau}\right].$$

Hence

$$\frac{dS_{AB}}{d\tau} = \frac{P_{AB}}{\tau} + \int_0^\tau \frac{\sigma_A - \sigma_B}{\tau}\, d\tau. \qquad \text{IV, 22.}$$

But from the equations of the thermo-electric circuit

$$\sigma_B - \sigma_A = \tau \frac{d^2 E_{AB}}{d\tau^2}$$

$$\int_0^\tau \frac{\sigma_B - \sigma_A}{\tau}\, d\tau = \frac{dE_{AB}}{d\tau} - \frac{dE_{AB}}{d\tau}\bigg|_{\tau=0}$$

and

$$\frac{P_{AB}}{\tau} = \frac{dE_{AB}}{d\tau}.$$

We have already seen that $\dfrac{dE_{AB}}{d\tau}\bigg|_{\tau=0} = 0$ by the third law, so that finally

$$\frac{dS_{AB}}{d\tau} = 0, \qquad \text{IV, 23.}$$

or the potential jump at the interface between two metals has at all temperatures the same value as at 0° Abs. In particular, this checks when applied to different orientations of the same crystal, for we have already seen that the potential jump at an interface vanishes at all temperatures.

The last result has at once a bearing on the hypothesis of Kelvin that the entire Volta jump is situated at the interface between the two metals. For if this were the case, S_{AB} would be equal to V_{AB}, and the temperature derivative of the Volta difference would vanish. By equation III, 10 this would demand that the surface heats of any pair of metals differ by their ordinary Peltier heat.

This is as far as I have been able to get by applying thermo-dynamics to the process of electron emission, treating the electron vapor as a perfect gas, but making no other assumptions about it. We can now go further and give a more explicit form to some of our expressions, and in particular to the expression 1 for the density of the electron vapor in equilibrium with the metal if we apply the third law of thermodynamics and quantum theory to the electron vapor.

Given a neutral metal at 0° Abs. We raise it to temperature τ and evaporate from it reversibly at this temperature a certain number of electrons, leaving behind a corresponding surface charge on the metal, together with, in general, a residue of neutral metal. For the purpose of the argument it is convenient to particularize by evaporating such a number of electrons that the original neutral metal is entirely used up, leaving as the final system only the electron vapor and surface charge. Any original metal in excess of this requirement will simply act as a dummy in the argument, cancelling from the final results. We now consider the entropy changes in the process just outlined. The entropy of the final system is the entropy of the electron vapor and surface charge. If we assume that the entropy of the original neutral metal was zero at 0° Abs, in accordance with the third law, then the final entropy is also the entropy imparted to the system in warming it to temperature and evaporating the electrons from it.

The entropy change during evaporation per electron is η/τ, where η is obviously the latent heat of evaporation in the isolated system, a surface charge being created during the evaporation. The entropy of the electron gas per electron is $S_0 + \frac{5}{2} \kappa \log \tau - \kappa \log p$. This expression holds for any gas, S_0 being the entropy at unit pressure and temperature. S_0 cannot be found by classical thermodynamics or by classical statistics, but quantum statistics permits an evaluation, and gives the value:

$$S_0 = \kappa \left(\frac{5}{2} + \log \frac{G(2\pi m)^{\frac{3}{2}} \kappa^{\frac{5}{2}}}{h^3} \right),$$ IV, 24.

where m is the mass of the electron and h Planck's constant. G is a weight factor; it was taken as unity in the original calculation of Sackur and Tetrode in which the electron was treated as a simple particle, but when electron spin is taken into account, it must be set equal to 2.

The entropy of the neutral metal at τ just before evaporation is $\int_0^\tau \frac{C_{pm}}{\tau} d\tau$, where C_{pm} is the specific heat at constant pressure of the metal. We are here neglecting the work done on the metal in compressing it to the pressure of the electron vapor; in view of the extreme minuteness of the latter this is entirely legitimate. Similarly the entropy of the surface charge is $\int_0^\tau \frac{C_{p\rho}}{\tau} d\tau$, if we apply the third law to it and assume that its entropy also vanishes at 0° Abs, or if we are unwilling to make this assumption, then its entropy is $S_{0\rho} + \int_0^\tau \frac{C_{p\rho}}{\tau} d\tau$. If we now equate the two different expressions for the entropy of the final system, we get:

$$\frac{5}{2}\kappa \log \tau - \kappa \log p + S_0 + S_{0\rho} + \int_0^\tau \frac{C_{p\rho}}{\tau} d\tau = \int_0^\tau \frac{C_{pm}}{\tau} d\tau + \frac{\eta}{\tau}.$$ IV, 25.

This may be solved for p, giving

$$p = G \frac{(2\pi m)^{\frac{3}{2}} \kappa^{\frac{5}{2}}}{h^3} \tau^{\frac{5}{2}} \epsilon^{\frac{5}{2} - \frac{\eta}{\kappa\tau} + \frac{S_{0\rho}}{\kappa} + \frac{1}{\kappa} \int_0^\tau \frac{C_{p\rho} - C_{pm}}{\tau} d\tau}.$$ IV, 26.

The exponent of the exponential may be further simplified by expressing η as a function of τ. We have the general thermodynamic relation

$$\frac{d\eta}{d\tau} = \frac{\eta}{\tau} - \frac{\eta}{\Delta v} \left(\frac{\partial \Delta v}{\partial \tau} \right)_p + \Delta C_p.$$ IV, 27.

This is a familiar thermodynamic relation which holds for any transition between two phases; it may be obtained by applying the first law to the cycle just considered. Δv is the difference of volume between the two phases, and ΔC_p is the difference of specific heat of the system before the transition and after it. To a high degree of approximation we may replace Δv by the volume of the electron vapor, or $\Delta v = v = \dfrac{\kappa \tau}{p}$, which gives

$$\left(\frac{\partial \, \Delta v}{\partial \tau} \right)_p = \frac{\kappa}{p}.$$

The first two terms of the right-hand side of equation 27 therefore cancel. ΔC_p for the usual transition consists of only two terms, the difference between the specific heat of vapor and solid. But here the solid is altered by the evaporation, a positive charge being left behind on the surface. This surface charge, in the absence of certain information to the contrary, must be assumed to have a specific heat of its own different from that of the metal, so that we must put $\Delta C_p = C_{pg} + C_{pp} - C_{pm}$, where the terms on the right are in succession the specific heats of gas, surface charge, and neutral metal. Since η is the latent heat per electron, C_{pg} refers to one electron in the gas, C_{pp} is the specific heat of the surface charge per positive ion, and C_{pm} is the specific heat of that number of atoms of the metal which give rise to one electron of vapor, that is, one atom if the atoms become singly ionized on evaporation of electrons, $\frac{1}{2}$ atom if they become doubly ionized, etc. For a perfect mon-atomic gas $C_p = \frac{5}{2} \kappa$; this holds even for the electron vapor because the vapor pressures are so excessively low that quantum effects are negligible. We have therefore:

$$\frac{d\eta}{d\tau} = \tfrac{5}{2} \kappa + C_{pp} - C_{pm}, \qquad \text{IV, 28.}$$

which gives on integration

$$\eta = \eta_0 + \tfrac{5}{2} \kappa \tau + \int_0^\tau (C_{pp} - C_{pm}) d\tau, \qquad \text{IV, 29.}$$

where η_0 is the value of η at $0°$ Abs.

The exponent of the natural base in equation 26, therefore, becomes

$$-\frac{\eta_0}{\kappa\tau} + \frac{S_{0\rho}}{\kappa} + \frac{1}{\kappa}\int_0^\tau \frac{C_{p\rho} - C_{pm}}{\tau}\,d\tau - \frac{1}{\kappa\tau}\int_0^\tau (C_{p\rho} - C_{pm})d\tau. \qquad \text{IV, 30.}$$

Write this as $-\dfrac{\eta_0}{\kappa\tau} + \log\alpha + \phi(\tau)$, where we have set $\dfrac{S_{0\rho}}{\kappa} = \log\alpha$, and the two integrals $= \phi(\tau)$, giving finally:

$$p = \frac{G\alpha\,(2\,\pi m)^{\frac{3}{2}}\kappa^{\frac{5}{2}}}{h^3}\,\tau^{\frac{5}{2}}\,\epsilon^{-\frac{\eta_0}{\kappa\tau} + \phi(\tau)}. \qquad \text{IV, 31.}$$

If our deduction has been correct, this should be essentially the same as equation 1 for n, the connection being $n = p/\kappa\tau$, except for the fact that the constant of equation 1 is not explicitly determined. It may in fact be verified by using the relation for $\dfrac{d\eta}{d\tau}$ that the constant of equation 1 may be given such a value as to reduce equation 1 identically to 31.

In principle, equation 31 contains only observable quantities, except for $G\alpha$. Given sufficient experimental skill, it should be possible by direct measurement of the electron vapor pressure as a function of temperature and of the other variables entering the equation to check the constancy of the factor $G\alpha$, and so check the equation. But direct measurement of the pertinent quantities is at present very far beyond experimental possibility, and we are forced to an indirect and partial verification of the equation. In particular, the equilibrium pressure cannot at present be measured, but we can measure instead the thermionic emission current, and get a connection between this and p by a theoretical argument. To get this connection we assume that the number of electrons emitted from the interior of the metal into the surrounding space is the same whether these are drawn away as fast as emitted, as in measuring thermionic emission, or whether they are allowed to accumulate in the space outside until the equilibrium pressure is built up. In the equilibrium condition we have a theoretical expression for the number of electrons approaching the surface of the metal, which must obviously be equal to the number leaving it. If we can assume that all the electrons leaving the surface come from the interior, that is, that there is no reflection at the internal surface of the electrons approaching it, then we have at once a connection between the emission current and the vapor pressure. The theoretical connection between gas pressure and number of electrons crossing unit surface in unit time, assuming Maxwell's distribution in the gas, is :

$$N = \frac{m\tau^{\frac{1}{2}}}{2\,\pi^{\frac{1}{2}}\kappa^{\frac{1}{2}}}\,p, \qquad\qquad \text{IV, 32.}$$

from which an expression for the thermionic emission current may at once be derived :

$$i \leqq \frac{2\,\pi\kappa^2 me}{h^3}\,(G\alpha)\tau^2\,\epsilon^{-\frac{\eta_0}{\kappa\tau}+\phi(\tau)}. \qquad\qquad \text{IV, 33.}$$

The equality sign obviously corresponds to the maximum possible emission current; if there is electron reflection in the equilibrium state, at the interior surface of the metal the number of electrons emitted from the interior of the metal is less than assumed above, and hence the current is less.

Experimentally it is known that thermionic emission for all pure metals can be represented by a formula of the type $i = $ Const $\tau^2\epsilon^{-b/\tau}$. The variation of the emission current with temperature is enormously rapid; this variation is carried by the exponential term in the formula. Because of this very rapid temperature variation it is extremely difficult to establish the other two factors, Const and τ^2, with much accuracy. It is known that exponents for τ varying from 1 to 3 or even more reproduce the results as well as the value 2. With regard to the constant factor, early derivations of the thermionic emission formula gave for the constant merely $\dfrac{2\,\pi\kappa^2 me}{h^3}$, without the factor G, because the existence of electron spin was not known at the time, and entirely neglecting the possible existence of the factor α. Now the curious fact is that for those metals for which measurements of thermionic emission are most satisfactory, W, Ta, and

Mo, the value for the Const seemed to be just $\frac{2\pi\kappa^2 me}{h^3}$, which corresponds to 60.2 amp/cm². The minimum possible value of the factor α is 1, corresponding to $S_{0\rho} = 0$, or zero entropy of the surface charge at 0° Abs. We may perhaps suppose that α is actually unity for *W*, *Ta*, and *Mo*. But now it is pretty certain that it is not legitimate to neglect the electron spin factor *G*, which has the value 2. Using this value, we can explain the observed value of the emission current by supposing that at least half the electrons which strike the surface are reflected. If α is greater than unity, then more than half must be reflected. It is not at all impossible that something of this sort actually occurs; analysis from the quantum point of view of the emission from the interior of the metal seems to demand something like this.

If the Const is greater than twice the value originally assigned to it, that is, greater than 120 amp/cm², then a value of α greater than unity is demanded. Such high values do seem to be demanded by some metals, notably platinum, although the question is not entirely free from experimental uncertainty. This means an entropy of the surface charge at 0° Abs greater than zero. Such is not surprising if it is considered that surface films are known to have the properties of a two-dimensional gas, and that the ions which compose the surface charge are doubtless distributed at random over the surface, their number being very small compared with that of the surface atoms, so that a regular arrangement would be difficult. Furthermore, if experiments are made on the same metal under different degrees of outgassing, that is, under different surface conditions, a connection is found between the " work function " and $G\alpha$. (In fact, the connection is linear.) Some connection between these quantities seems consistent with the physical picture.

Let us now fasten our attention on the exponential part of the emission formula, where the accuracy is high, and inquire what is the significance of the fact that the exponent is of the form $-b/\tau$. We must have:

$$-\frac{\eta_0}{\kappa\tau} + \frac{1}{\kappa}\left[\int_0^\tau \frac{\zeta}{\tau}\,d\tau - \frac{1}{\tau}\int_0^\tau \zeta\,d\tau\right] \equiv -\frac{b}{\tau},$$

abbreviating $C_{p\rho} - C_{pm}$ by ζ. Differentiate this equation by τ, obtaining

$$\frac{\eta_0}{\kappa\tau^2} + \frac{1}{\kappa}\left[\frac{1}{\tau^2}\int^\tau \zeta \, d\tau\right] \equiv \frac{b}{\tau^2}.$$

Multiply by τ^2, and differentiate again, obtaining

$$\zeta = 0,$$

or

$$C_{p\rho} - C_{pm} = 0. \qquad\qquad \text{IV, 34.}$$

Hence, independent of assumption of electron reflection at the surface, or uncertainty about the effect of electron spin, the specific heat of neutral metal and surface charge must be equal to each other if the emission formula is to have the observed exponential form.

There is a connection between $C_{p\rho} - C_{pm}$ and the surface heats. Combine equation 7 with equation 15, obtaining

$$\frac{d\eta}{d\tau} + e\frac{dP_S}{d\tau} + e\left(\sigma - \frac{P_S}{\tau}\right) = \frac{\gamma\kappa}{\gamma - 1} = \tfrac{5}{2}\,\kappa. \qquad \text{IV, 35.}$$

But we also have

$$\frac{d\eta}{d\tau} = \tfrac{5}{2}\,\kappa + C_{p\rho} - C_{pm}.$$

Eliminating $d\eta/d\tau$,

$$C_{p\rho} - C_{pm} = -e\left[\frac{dP_S}{d\tau} + \sigma - \frac{P_S}{\tau}\right] = -e\left[\sigma + \tau\frac{d}{d\tau}\left(\frac{P_S}{\tau}\right)\right], \quad \text{IV, 36.}$$

a connection between surface heat, specific heat, and Thomson heat. If $C_{p\rho} - C_{pm} = 0$, as the emission formula would suggest, we have a connection between the surface heat and Thomson heat,

$$\frac{d}{d\tau}\left(\frac{P_S}{\tau}\right) = -\frac{\sigma}{\tau},$$

or, on integration,

$$P_S = \tau\int_0^\tau -\frac{\sigma \, d\tau}{\tau} + \text{Const}, \qquad\qquad \text{IV, 37.}$$

and the surface heat is simply connected with the driving e.m.f.

We may further obtain information about the Volta difference of potential between two metals whose thermionic emission formulas contain the exponential term $e^{-b/\tau}$, independent of the value of the coefficient. For all such metals $C_{p\rho} - C_{pm} = 0$, and equation 29 becomes

$$\eta_A = \eta_{0A} + \tfrac{5}{2} \kappa \tau.$$

Write this equation for the two metals, and subtract, obtaining

$$\eta_A - \eta_B = \eta_{0A} - \eta_{0B}.$$

But we also have

$$\eta_A - \eta_B = e \left(V_{BA} + \tau \frac{dV_{BA}}{d\tau} \right).$$

Substitution and integration gives:

$$V_{AB} = \frac{1}{e} (\eta_{0B} - \eta_{0A}) + c\tau = V_{0AB} + c\tau, \qquad \text{IV, 38.}$$

where c is an undetermined constant of integration. V_{AB} is therefore a linear function of temperature for such metals.

CHAPTER V

THE EFFECT OF SURFACE CHARGE ON VAPOR PRES-SURE, AND ELECTRON EMISSION UNDER INTENSE FIELDS

Experimentally it is well established that if a sufficiently strong electric field is applied perpendicularly to the surface of a metal, an electron current is emitted by the metal. The natural picture of this phenomenon is that the electrons are pulled away from or " out of " the metal by the intense field. This phenomenon has usually been considered to be entirely beyond attack by classical methods, as perhaps indicated by the fact that even under ordinary conditions the force which restrains the charge on the surface against the " boiler pressure," $2 \pi \rho^2$, must be described as a " non-electrostatic " force. The problem has been recently attacked by the methods of wave mechanics and expressions deduced for the current as a function of the field which are not wide of the mark.[8] The subject is one of great difficulty experimentally, however, since it has been impossible up to the present to get values for the cold emission current which are truly characteristic of the metal and not affected by geometrical irregularities in the surface, and these are practically impossible to eliminate or reproduce on the scale of dimensions required. It seemed to me, however, that certain aspects of this problem should be open to attack by classical methods, since in the Volta effect we have the possibility of producing fields of any desired intensity by bringing two metals close enough together, and at constant temperature the mechanism of the Volta effect is con-servative and reversible and therefore amenable to thermody-namic analysis. I published a paper [9] in which the very intense fields which may be produced in this way were considered, and I drew certain conclusions. One of these conclusions was most paradoxical, namely, that the density of an electron vapor immediately outside the surface of a metal was changed to the same extent by a field of given numerical magnitude independent of the direction of the field, that is, whether the field was pulling the electrons away from the surface or driving them into it. This result by itself should have suggested that the phenomenon analyzed by the use of the Volta effect was not the same as the phenomenon of cold emission. I have now been able to carry the analysis further and to find an explicit formula for the effect of normal field on the vapor pressure of the electrons in equilibrium; the electron vapor pressure is given by an exponential in the square of the field (or surface charge). It is therefore now certain that cold emission must be something quite different.

In the following I give the simple analysis for the effect of normal field (or surface charge) on ordinary vapor pressure. There is a certain intrinsic interest in this problem, which I have not seen discussed anywhere, in spite of the fact that the analysis does not have the application originally intended. We consider first the effect of normal field on vaporization when the vapor is electrically neutral; an example would be the effect of charging the surface of a pool or mercury on the pressure of the mercury vapor in equilibrium with it.

Construct a condenser of two parallel plates of the same metal and connect the plates to a perfectly reversible electromagnetic

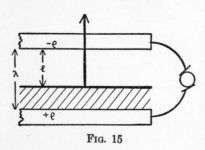

FIG. 15

engine by which the plates may be charged to any desired difference of potential. Cover the upper plate with an impervious neutral membrane, by which formation of vapor at this plate is prevented. Allow vapor to form freely at the lower plate and come to the equilibrium pressure in the space immediately above

it. In the space between the condenser plates insert a piston, which is exposed to the vapor pressure, and which may be moved at pleasure by a suitable external mechanical agency (Figure 15). Let l be the distance from upper condenser plate to the piston, and λ from upper condenser plate to the upper surface of the lower plate. The plates are to be held rigidly in some sort of a frame, so that no external work is done corresponding to a change of distance between the plates, λ changing only because of condensation of vapor on the lower plate or evaporation from it. As independent variables fixing the condition of the system we may conveniently choose absolute temperature, τ, surface charge, ρ, on the lower plate, and l, the position of the piston. We have taken the surface charge as the variable instead of the normal field because it is somewhat easier to handle; the two are evidently equivalent, since $\mathcal{E}_n = 4\pi\rho$. The following analysis applies to unit area of the plate.

The general method employed is exactly the same as applied in Chapter III to the Volta condenser. Write

$$dQ = dU + dW,$$

where Q is heat absorbed and U internal energy. Work can be done by this system only by movement of the charge through the external engine, or by motion of the piston.

Hence, $\qquad dW = -V\,d\rho - p\,dl,$

where V is difference of potential between the plates and p vapor pressure. $V = 4\pi\rho\lambda$, neglecting the very small dielectric constant of the vapor. Express the differentials in terms of the independent variables:

$$dQ = \frac{\partial U}{\partial \tau}\,d\tau + \frac{\partial U}{\partial \rho}\,d\rho + \frac{\partial U}{\partial l}\,dl - 4\pi\rho\lambda\,d\rho - p\,dl.$$

Divide by τ, thus forming dS, the differential of entropy, and express the condition that this is a perfect differential. There are 3 conditions.

(1) Condition on the coefficients of τ and ρ.

$$\frac{\partial}{\partial \rho}\left(\frac{1}{\tau}\frac{\partial U}{\partial \tau}\right) = \frac{1}{\tau}\left[\frac{\partial U}{\partial \rho} - 4\pi\rho\lambda\right] - \frac{1}{\tau^2}\frac{\partial Q}{\partial \rho},$$

which gives, almost at once,

$$\frac{\partial \lambda}{\partial \tau} = -\frac{1}{\tau}\cdot\frac{1}{4\pi\rho}\cdot\frac{\partial Q}{\partial \rho}. \qquad\qquad \text{V, 1.}$$

This result is not of any immediate interest to us; it is evident that $\frac{\partial \lambda}{\partial \tau}$ is not identically zero because of evaporation when temperature changes, and $\frac{\partial Q}{\partial \rho}$ evidently includes a heat of vaporization if the vapor pressure changes when surface charge changes.

(2) Condition on coefficients of τ and λ.

$$\frac{\partial}{\partial l}\left(\frac{1}{\tau}\frac{\partial U}{\partial \tau}\right) = \frac{1}{\tau}\frac{\partial}{\partial \tau}\left[\frac{\partial U}{\partial l} - p\right] - \frac{1}{\tau^2}\frac{\partial Q}{\partial l},$$

which reduces at once to :

$$\frac{\partial p}{\partial \tau} = -\frac{1}{\tau}\frac{\partial Q}{\partial l}. \qquad \text{V, 2.}$$

This is the exact analog of Clapeyron's equation.

(3) Condition on coefficients of ρ and l.

$$\frac{\partial}{\partial l}\left[\frac{\partial U}{\partial \rho} - 4\pi\rho\lambda\right] = \frac{\partial}{\partial \rho}\left[\frac{\partial U}{\partial l} - p\right],$$

which gives at once :

$$\frac{\partial p}{\partial \rho} = 4\pi\rho\frac{\partial \lambda}{\partial l}, \qquad \text{V, 3.}$$

the desired relation involving an effect of surface charge on vapor pressure. It is at once evident that the sign of $\partial p/\partial \rho$ is negative, since λ decreases, because of condensation of vapor, when l increases.

This equation may be integrated if the vapor satisfies the perfect gas law. Push the piston in far enough to condense one atom of vapor. $d\lambda = -v_{sol}$, where v_{sol} is the volume of one atom of the solid. Furthermore, if v is the volume of one atom of gas $(pv = \kappa\tau)$,

$$(\lambda + d\lambda) - (l + dl) - (\lambda - l) = -v,$$

or

$$dl = v - v_{sol}.$$

Whence

$$\frac{\partial \lambda}{\partial l} = -\frac{v_{sol}}{v - v_{sol}} \approx -\frac{v_{sol}}{v}. \qquad \text{V, 4.}$$

The last approximation is sufficient because v_{sol} is very much less than v. Hence, substituting,

$$\frac{\partial p}{\partial \rho} = -\, 4\,\pi\rho\,\frac{v_{sol}}{v} = -\,\frac{4\,\pi\rho p}{\kappa\tau}\,v_{sol}. \qquad\qquad V, 5.$$

v_{sol} may be treated with sufficient accuracy as a constant independent of ρ and τ. The equation may be integrated at once, giving,

$$p = p_0(\tau)\epsilon^{-\frac{2\,\pi v_{sol}}{\kappa\tau}\rho^2}, \qquad\qquad V, 6.$$

where p_0 is the normal vapor pressure with no surface charge.

The vapor pressure decreases, therefore, exponentially as the square of the surface charge, becoming zero for infinite surface charge. This effect is purely a result of the change in internal pressure in the solid phase due to the presence on it of the surface charge. It is a familiar result of elementary thermodynamics that if the pressure on liquid or solid phase only is increased, the excess pressure not acting on the vapor, the vapor pressure is thereby increased by a factor equal to the ratio of volume of condensed phase to volume of vapor phase multiplied into the increase of pressure. Here the internal pressure of the condensed phase is *decreased* by the boiler pressure $2\,\pi\rho^2$ tending to blow the charge off the surface and producing an equilibrating *tension* in the interior of the condensed phase. Under actual conditions the effect is, of course, very small because the volume of the vapor is so much greater than that of the solid. It may be calculated that at 300° Abs a charge of 8 E.S.U. per unit area on mercury, corresponding to a normal field of 30,000 volts per cm, decreases the vapor pressure by 1.2×10^{-7}.

Our result may at once be applied to the electron vapor in equilibrium with a metal, replacing v_{sol} by $v_{sol} - v_\rho$, where v_ρ is the volume of so much surface charge as corresponds to one electron in the vapor. No appreciable error is made by neglecting the space charge in the vapor. It is, however, to be noted that the moving pistons of the analysis above must be kept so close to the evaporating surface that the addition to the normal gas pressure arising from the acceleration of the electrons in the field may be neglected. This is a purely mechanical effect, with no thermal aspects, and would only complicate the analysis if it were included. There is no experimental evidence of the sign of $v_{sol} - v_{\rho}$, so that it is not inconceivable that the electron vapor pressure may be increased by a surface charge, instead of decreasing like an ordinary vapor. One would expect, however, v_{sol} and v_{ρ} not to be markedly different, and therefore the effect on electron vapor pressure to be even smaller than on ordinary vapor pressure.

The result of my original analysis is thus verified, namely, that the effect is independent of the sign of the surface charge, that is, independent of the direction of the normal field. Cold emission is therefore an essentially different sort of phenomenon from that considered here, and is undoubtedly connected with various quantum effects. It is probably not legitimate to picture the electron as a point charge or the surface of the plate as a uniquely defined plane surface in the realm of magnitudes pertinent to this phenomenon. In fact, if one calculates the wave length of the electron under these conditions, it will be found to be of the same order of magnitude as the distance between the plates necessary to give rise, by the Volta effect, to fields of sufficient intensity to produce cold emission.

However, the analysis above has, I believe, one suggestion as to current wave mechanics treatments of this phenomenon. The intense normal field must give rise to a surface charge; this surface charge is neglected in the wave mechanics treatments, and in fact I have never seen a description in wave mechanics terms (altered distribution of the ψ function) of the surface charge. One cannot help feeling intuitively that the surface charge must play some part in the phenomenon.

CHAPTER VI

THERMO–ELECTRIC PHENOMENA IN CRYSTALS

The fundamental fact with respect to crystals has already been used in Chapter III, namely, that single metal crystals, except those crystallizing in the cubic system, are thermo-electrically non-isotropic, so that rods cut from a crystal in different directions behave toward each other thermo-electrically like different metals. It is to be noticed at once that this fact reduces the law of Magnus to a purely academic position, except for liquid or cubic metals, for in any actual wire of a non-cubic metal the size of the single crystal grains is finite in comparison with the dimensions of the wire, so that the crystal arrangement cannot be absolutely haphazard for all possible distributions of the temperature gradient, and a sensitive enough measuring device must detect residual effects determined by the preponderant crystal orientation.

In Chapter III the simple case was examined in which the rods were cut either parallel or perpendicular to the principal axis of the crystal. In the general case there are much more complicated phenomena; these we shall consider here. This discussion will be from an elementary point of view, in which emphasis is laid on the qualitative nature of the phenomena in various simple cases. A complete description of thermo-electric phenomena, not only in crystals, but in any sort of non-isotropic and non-homogeneous material, has been thrown into exceedingly elegant and compact form, using tensor analysis, by Ehrenfest and Rutgers.[10] In the last part of this chapter a résumé of their analysis is given. I have preferred, however, the emphasis on the fundamental physical phenomena which is given by a less elegant analysis. A treatment of thermo-electric phenomena in crystals was first given in complete form by Kelvin.[11] His treatment was also formal to a certain extent. His analysis enabled him to predict the existence of an effect peculiar to crystals, a transverse heating effect, but, on the other hand, he overlooked another most interesting phenomenon, the internal Peltier heat. That a man of Kelvin's profound physical intuition should have failed to draw this consequence from his analysis illustrates the danger in any analysis which is confined too much to purely formal manipulations.

Consider a thermo-couple one of whose branches is a long slender rod cut in any direction from the crystal, and the other

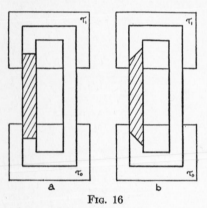

FIG. 16

branch is some isotropic metal. This couple gives a thermal E.M.F. dependent only on the orientation of the rod, the isotropic metal, and the temperatures of the junctions. The E.M.F. is independent of the method of connection between crystal rod and isotropic metal, provided the connection is all made in a region at constant temperature, and is in particular not dependent on whether the crystal rod is cut at an angle at the connecting surface as shown in Figure 16, *a*, or is cut square as in Figure 16, *b*. The fact that no rearrangements of the circuit in the region all at constant temperature can have any effect on the net E.M.F. is a consequence of the second law of thermodynamics. For if there were such an effect, then we could construct a system composed only of the two different arrangements, all at the same temperature, which would give a net E.M.F., and this would be contrary to the second law, because isothermal systems, in which no material changes are taking place, cannot deliver energy.

In order not to unduly complicate the following discussion it will pay to state at the beginning that all known metals crystallize in geometrical forms with at least one principal axis of rotational symmetry, and in fact the axis is either of three-, or four-, or six-fold symmetry; two-fold principal axes are not known for metals. It is also an experimental fact that the two ends of the principal axis of rotational symmetry are similar, which means that any axis perpendicular to the principal axis is an axis of two-fold symmetry. If we accept Neumann's law that all physical phenomena must be of at least as high symmetry as the external geometrical figure of the crystal, then thermo-electric phenomena must have at least one axis of three-, four-, or six-fold symmetry in all metals. This is, as a matter of experiment, the case, and we shall assume it in the following. If the crystal is cubic (three axes at right angles of four-fold symmetry), then it is thermo-electrically isotropic, and need not be considered here.

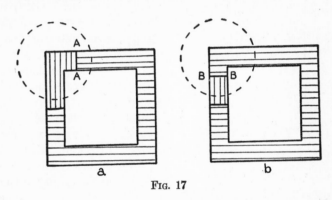

FIG. 17

The mere existence of a thermal E.M.F. in a circuit composed of rods cut parallel and perpendicular to the axis (we need not for the present consider the question as to whether the longitude of the rod in the plane perpendicular to the principal axis makes any difference) demands the existence of a new thermal effect, peculiar to crystals. Consider the two circuits of Figure 17, cut from the same crystal, but differently oriented, as shown. Maintain each circuit at constant temperature and circulate a current about it. The second law demands that the net reversible heating effects in each circuit be zero. Now the one circuit differs from the other only in the part within the dotted lines. The heating effect in the parts outside the dotted lines are therefore the same, which demands that the heating effects within the dotted lines also be the same. Now there is certainly a Peltier heat at the surfaces of discontinuity of orientation AA and BB, and the heats at these surfaces are certainly different, the current in one case passing from parallel to perpendicular and in the other from perpendicular to parallel. There must therefore be other compensating heating effects, and the principle of sufficient reason, reinforced by elementary considerations of crystal symmetry, shows that the only possible place for such an effect is in the body of the metal at the corner where the direction of current flow changes. We must, therefore, in general recognize the existence of a reversible heating effect in the body of a crystal where the direction of current flow changes. This I have called the "internal" Peltier heat. It has the same dimensions as the regular Peltier heat, that is, it is a heat per unit quantity of electricity, independent of the strength of the current. Expressed in terms of electrons, this means that every electron that turns the corner in the crystal must absorb the same amount of heat, whether it is moving rapidly, as perhaps in a heavy current, or slowly in a small current. This means further that if an electron is moving in a definite direction in a crystal and is slowly brought to rest, it cannot be started moving again, no matter how slowly, in any other direction without the absorption of a definite and finite amount of thermal energy. This evidently demands the existence of some sort of fine structure in the crystal not at all contemplated by the ordinary large-scale equations.

We can get an exact expression for the internal Peltier heat in terms of the ordinary Peltier heat at the interfaces in this simple case. Call the internal Peltier heat when the direction of current flow in the metal changes from perpendicular to parallel to the axis $I_{\perp\parallel}$. Then setting the total heat generated in the dotted regions of Figures 17, a and 17, b equal to each other gives at once :

$$P_{\parallel\perp} + I_{\perp\parallel} = I_{\parallel\perp} + P_{\perp\parallel}.$$

Whence, since $I_{\perp\parallel} = -I_{\parallel\perp}$ and $P_{\parallel\perp} = -P_{\perp\parallel}$,

$$I_{\perp\parallel} = P_{\perp\parallel}. \qquad\qquad \text{VI, 1.}$$

We next consider the relation between the thermal E.M.F. and the orientation with respect to the crystal, that is, the symmetry relations. This question was considered by Kelvin, who found it necessary to make a special assumption in order to make any progress. This he called " the axiom of the superposition of thermo-electric effects," and is that the heating effect of any current is the same as the sum of the effects which would be produced by its vector components separately, no matter what the method of resolution of current into components. This assumption is at once seen to be consistent with the simplest expression for the complete reversibility of the heating effects. If the heating effects are reversible, they must reverse sign when the sign of the current changes, and the simplest dependence on current with this property is linear dependence. Experimentally, no higher order terms, which must be of odd degree, have been detected. Kelvin's assumption, which is that the heating effects are linear and additive in the components of the current, certainly satisfies this demand of reversibility, but it is not the only way of satisfying it, as may be seen by the following very simple example. Consider these two expressions for a heating effect in terms of the rectangular components :

(a) Heat $= c_1 i_x + c_2 i_y + c_3 i_z$.

(b) Heat $= c_1 \dfrac{i_x^3}{i_x^2 + i_y^2 + i_z^2} + c_2 \dfrac{i_y^3}{i_x^2 + i_y^2 + i_z^2} + c_3 \dfrac{i_z^3}{i_x^2 + i_y^2 + i_z^2}$.

The first is reversible and linear in the total current, for if every current component is multiplied by a constant factor, the total heating effect is multiplied by the same factor, and in addition satisfies Kelvin's assumption of additivity, while the second is also reversible and linear in the total current, but is not additive, as one sees by adding the heating effects obtained by setting in succession i_x, i_y, and i_z the only component. Thermodynamics and reversibility demands only expressions of the form (b), and there are evidently an infinite number of analytical expressions satisfying this demand. Kelvin's assumption is therefore a real assumption, additional to the fundamental assumption of perfect reversibility, and must be tested by experiment. Doubtless Kelvin was led to it intuitively by analogy with other phenomena of currents. For example, the magnetic field surrounding a current is the vector sum of the magnetic fields produced by the components of the current, or the Joulean heating by any current is the sum of the Joulean heating of its rectangular components. But the Joulean heating is not additive for *any* method of resolution, for obviously if the current is resolved into two currents, each equal to one half the original current, the sum of the heating effects is only one half the total. It is furthermore to be noticed that if, in the thermo-electric case, the heating for any direction of the current involves odd powers of the current higher than the first, Kelvin's assumption cannot possibly hold.

In order now to derive the symmetry relations, accepting Kelvin's axiom, we split the current flowing lengthwise in a bar cut obliquely to the axis into two components parallel and perpendicular to the axis. The question as to the difference between bars of the same azimuth but different longitudes with respect to the crystal axis can be answered after this present discussion. For the moment we may assume that the longitude of the bar designated by ⊥ is the same as that of the oblique bar under discussion. We notice in the first place that if the current flows

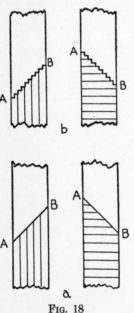

Fig. 18

parallel to the length in a rod cut either parallel or perpendicular to the axis, there can be no heating effects at the lateral surfaces of the bar, for the symmetry of the crystal allows no differentiation of the lateral surfaces by which a heating might be determined at one and a cooling at the other. To prove this it is necessary to use the fact that all axes at right angles to the principal axis are of two-fold symmetry. The existence of a lateral heating effect in crystals was first deduced by Kelvin, and it is perhaps anticipating to mention it here, but it will be seen that our method of proof needs the fact that it vanishes for the two directions parallel and perpendicular.

It now follows from the absence of any heating effect at the lateral faces that the total Peltier heat absorbed at the interface of separation when current emerges from a crystal rod into an isotropic medium is independent of the orientation of the interface with respect to the length of the rod, provided the rod is either parallel or perpendicular to the axis. That is, in Figure 18, *a*, the heat absorbed at the surface *AB* when unit quantity flows along the rod is independent of the orientation of the surface *AB*. Or if the interface is given the form of a series of rectangular steps, as in Figure 18, *b*, the heat absorbed is still the same. It is important to notice that this is not true when the orientation is neither parallel nor perpendicular.

Consider now the heating at the interface between an isotropic metal and a slender crystal rod with the principal axis inclined at an angle θ to the length, as in Figure 19. We assume that the rod is of square section, of unit side, with depth perpendicular to the plane of the paper, and with the crystal axis in the plane of the paper. The interface between crystal and isotropic metal

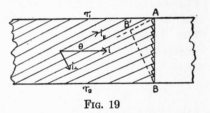

Fig. 19

is to be perpendicular to the length of the rod. There is a heating effect at the interface which depends on the angle θ, because it is known experimentally that the total E.M.F. of a thermocouple depends on the orientation. Furthermore, *all* the *net* heating effect is at this surface because, although symmetry allows heating effects at the two transverse surfaces perpendicular to the plane of the paper, symmetry also demands that the signs at the two surfaces be opposite, and since we have drawn *AB* perpendicular to the length, the areas of the two transverse surfaces are equal, and hence their total contribution to the net heating effect vanishes. Call the heating effect at *AB* under these conditions $P_{\theta m}$, *m* denoting the isotropic metal. Let the longitudinal current density be i, and resolve i into two components, $i_{\parallel}$, parallel, and $i_{\perp}$, perpendicular to the principal axis.

$$i_{\parallel} = i \cos \theta,$$
$$i_{\perp} = i \sin \theta.$$

According to Kelvin's axiom, the sum of the heating effects of these two components on crossing AB is to be equal to the heating effect of i, or $iP_{\theta m}$. But now we have just seen that the contribution of $i_{\parallel}$ in crossing AB is, since there is no contribution on AB', the same as its contribution in crossing BB', or the step-like surface, and this is evidently the product of the total current parallel to the axis and $P_{\parallel m}$, or $i_{\parallel} \cos \theta P_{\parallel m}$. Similarly, the total contribution by the perpendicular component is $i_{\perp} \sin \theta P_{\perp m}$. Substituting the values of $i_{\parallel}$ and $i_{\perp}$, and setting the sum $= iP_{\theta m}$, gives at once:

$$P_{\theta m} = \cos^2\theta \, P_{\parallel m} + \sin^2 \theta \, P_{\perp m}$$
$$= (P_{\parallel m} - P_{\perp m}) \cos^2 \theta + P_{\perp m}, \qquad \text{VI, 2.}$$

and the heating effect at a surface perpendicular to the length of the rod, which makes an angle θ with the principal axis, is a linear function of $\cos^2 \theta$. This is one of Kelvin's symmetry relations.

We can obviously get rid of the isotropic metal m by replacing it by another piece of crystal cut, let us say, with axis perpendicular to the length. Then

$$P_{\perp m} = P_{\perp\perp} \equiv 0,$$

and,

$$P_{\theta\perp} = P_{\parallel\perp} \cos^2 \theta. \qquad \text{VI, 3.}$$

Or, the subscript m in equation 2 is usually suppressed, and equation 2 is then written:

$$P_\theta = (P_\parallel - P_\perp) \cos^2 \theta + P_\perp, \qquad \text{VI, 4.}$$

the meaning of the notation being sufficiently plain. It is obvious that P for every orientation is increased by a constant when one isotropic metal replaces another.

Consider next what happens at the lateral surface perpendicular to the plane of the paper. There is actually no transverse current flow across the lateral faces, so that we cannot in general talk of an ordinary Peltier heat at this interface. However, by the aid of an ingenious device due to Kelvin, this is possible under our present conditions. Imagine the crystal imbedded on both sides in the isotropic metal, and the uniform current density i flowing everywhere. There is no flow across the transverse boundary, and since there are no heating effects in the isotropic metal itself, the heating effects are everywhere the same as in the actual problem in which no isotropic metal touches the transverse faces. But now each of the components $i_\parallel$ and $i_\perp$ has by itself components of lateral flow, and therefore lateral heating effects due to the corresponding Peltier heats. The total lateral heating effect is the sum of the contributions of the components. The total amount of current carried by $i_\parallel$ across unit area of the upper transverse surface is $i_\parallel \sin \theta$, and therefore the total heating effect per unit area due to this component is

$$i_\parallel \sin \theta \, P_{\parallel m} = i \sin \theta \cos \theta \, P_{\parallel m}.$$

At the upper surface $i_\perp$ flows into the crystal from m and the total generation of heat by it per unit area is

$$i_\perp \cos \theta \, P_{m\perp} = i \cos \theta \sin \theta \, P_{m\perp}.$$

Hence by Kelvin's axiom at the upper transverse surface there is a net generation of heat per unit area per unit time of :

$$T = i \cos \theta \sin \theta \, (P_{\parallel m} - P_{\perp m}) = i \cos \theta \sin \theta \, P_{\parallel \perp}. \quad \text{VI, 5.}$$

At the lower surface there is a numerically equal generation, but of the opposite sign, the direction of flow of each component with respect to the isotropic metal being, of course, reversed.

The positive generation of heat at one transverse face and an equal absorption at the other face results in a transverse temperature gradient, just sufficient to carry the heat across the crystal by ordinary thermal conduction. The rod, therefore, comes to a steady state, with one face permanently warmer than the surroundings and the other cooler.

This transverse heating effect was predicted by Kelvin in 1857 on the basis of analysis essentially equivalent to the above. It was first demonstrated experimentally in bismuth by Borelius and Lindh [12] in 1917, and was subsequently independently announced by me [13] in 1927, and in the same year by Terada and Tsutsui. [14] The effect is large enough for easy experimental demonstration. With a rod of bismuth 6 mm in diameter and a total current of 1 amp, temperature differences of 0.5° may be set up between opposite transverse faces. The effect is evidently a maximum when the axis is at 45° to the length.

There is no transverse heating effect on the lateral faces in the plane of the paper of Figure 19; this is evidently not allowed by the crystal symmetry. The heating effect on any lateral face not having either of these two orientations is to be found by resolving the face into two, perpendicular and parallel to the face of maximum generation, which is the face in the plane perpendicular to the plane of the axis and the length.

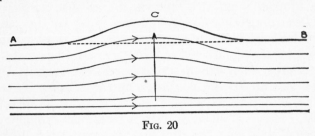

Fig. 20

The existence of a lateral surface effect demands the existence of another kind of internal heating. Imagine a crystal with a central bulge, as in Figure 20. The total heating between A and B must be the same as if the section of the crystal had been uniform in this region, as shown by the dotted line; that is, the total heating is the same as the lateral heating between A and B of the uniform rod. By making the bulge fat enough, the current density at the periphery ACB may be made vanishingly small, and so the transverse heating at the boundary may be made to vanish. The internal heating from change of direction cancels by symmetry throughout the region, symmetrically situated elements on the entrance and exit sides making equal and opposite contributions. There is left only a body effect in the region where the current density changes in the direction at right angles to the flow. That is, if there are terms $\partial i_x / \partial y$ in the current distribution, a volume heating is to be expected in general. The equations for body distribution developed by Ehrenfest and Rutgers give an explicit formulation of this effect. So far as I know, this effect has not been sought for experimentally.

The question as to the variation with longitude about the prin cipal axis may now at once be settled. The argument already given may be repeated, replacing the rods parallel and perpendicular by two rods perpendicular to each other, but cut from the plane perpendicular to the principal axis. It may be seen at once by symmetry that directions are possible in this plane for which any transverse heats must vanish. Chose one of these directions as a direction of reference, corresponding to the parallel or perpendicular of the preceding analysis. This analysis may be now repeated and a formula exactly like 2 obtained. But for a crystal with a four-fold axis it is obvious at once that the Peltier heat for any two directions at right angles must be the same, and hence at once by the analog of formula 2, P must be the same in all orientations in this plane. If the crystal has three- or six-fold symmetry, then symmetry demands the equality of P for two directions at 60° to each other, and this, again by the same formula, is only possible when P is the same for all directions in the plane. Hence in all cases there is rotational symmetry about the principal axis, and the formulas just developed hold for all longitudes, so that another subscript to show the longitude is superfluous. It is to be noticed that this proof of rotational symmetry also involves Kelvin's axiom; without the axiom I have not been able to find any necessary variation of thermo-electric properties either in azimuth or longitude.

The experimental check of Kelvin's two symmetry relations for the Peltier heat and the transverse heat has not been made the object of any extensive inquiry by many investigators. The relation for the Peltier heat is certainly verified to a small margin of error, but in the cases of tin and bismuth I have found distinct departures from the $\cos^2 \theta$ relation which seemed to me to be beyond experimental error.[15] Whether these departures will prove to be real on more exhaustive measurements by other observers cannot at present be told. One thing is to be noted in this connection, namely, that if either the total E.M.F. of a couple, or the Peltier heat, or the Thomson heat, is proved to be linear in $\cos^2 \theta$ at every temperature, then the other two must be linear also. This can be proved at once by integration or differentiation of the thermo-electric equations with respect to temperature.

The rotational symmetry of P, that is, the fact that the thermo-electric quality of every rod cut perpendicular to the principal axis is the same, seems to be verified within experimental error, but the experimental accuracy is considerably less than for change of azimuth.

A quantitative examination of the symmetry of the transverse heats has been made only by Stabler [16] for bismuth. He found systematic and consistent deviations from Kelvin's relation, but I believe he is not convinced that the effect is real, but thinks it may be due to some systematic imperfection in the crystal. It is also pertinent to add that Uehling [16] has given a theoretical kinetic derivation of the Kelvin symmetry relation under very general assumptions, but retaining the classical picture of the electron as a discrete point charge.

At any rate, as far as present experimental evidence goes, there can be no doubt that Kelvin's relations are a close approximation to the facts.

The existence of the transverse heat involves other interesting consequences. There is in the first place an inverse effect, that is, if a temperature difference is set up between transverse faces of a crystal rod, there is a longitudinal E.M.F. which generates a current along the rod if the two ends are connected. This is very easily demonstrated. The magnitude of the transverse E.M.F. is easily calculated by an analysis exactly like that used in deriving the equations of an ordinary thermo-electric circuit, allowing the irreversible processes to take place. Consider a bar of rectangular section of breadth b and unit depth in which a current of density i flows, and in which there is a transverse generation and absorption of heat at the two opposite faces of amount T per unit area per unit current density. If the transverse thermal conductivity is κ_t, a transverse temperature difference will be set up of amount iTb/κ_t. In unit time the amount of heat iT per unit length passes by conduction from one side of the plate to the other, resulting in an increase of entropy of the universe of

$$\frac{iT}{\tau^2}\left(\frac{iTb}{\kappa_t}\right) \equiv \frac{1}{\tau^2}\frac{T^2 i^2 b}{\kappa_t}. \qquad\qquad \text{VI, 6}$$

This increase of entropy must manifest itself as an increase of temperature of the whole system, and this can be brought about only by the current working against an additional E.M.F. brought into existence by the transverse temperature gradient. If we call the E.M.F. per unit length per unit transverse temperature gradient e_t, the total E.M.F. per unit length is in this case $e_t i T / \kappa_t$, and the total energy delivered by it is $e_t i^2 T b / \kappa_t$, and the corresponding increase of entropy $e_t i^2 T b / (\kappa_t \tau)$. Equating the two expressions for the entropy gives:

$$e_t = \frac{T}{\tau}. \qquad \text{VI, 7.}$$

This transverse E.M.F. is evidently what we have called a " working " e.m.f. The sources of energy supply are evidently thermal. If then a temperature difference is maintained between opposite transverse faces and a longitudinal current allowed to flow, the work done by the E.M.F. driving this current must be provided by the net heat input. We may look for this at the transverse faces or in the body of the metal, between the faces. Let us in the first place assume that it is all in the transverse faces. This means that the T at one face is different from that at the other; there is evidently such an effect, for one face is warmer than the other, and T may be a temperature function. The difference of transverse heat at the two faces is $\Delta \tau \frac{d}{d\tau} (iT)$. The work done by the E.M.F. is $e_t (iT/\kappa_t)(ib)$. Equating these two and substituting for e_t and $\Delta \tau$ the values T/τ and iTb/κ_t gives

$$\frac{dT}{d\tau} = \frac{T}{\tau}, \text{ or } T = \text{Const } \tau.$$

But this, by 5, would demand that $P_\parallel - P_\perp$ be proportional to absolute temperature, and this we know in general not to be the case. The situation is exactly analogous to that in the analysis of the ordinary thermo-electric circuit when we assumed that the Peltier heat provided the entire E.M.F. of the circuit. We were then confronted with a contradiction which forced us to assume another heating effect, the Thomson heat. Similarly here, there must be another heating effect, and the only place for it is in the body of the metal, where there is a temperature gradient. This means that when a current flows lengthwise in a crystal rod

across which there is a temperature gradient there is a generation of heat within the body of the metal. The magnitude of
this transverse Thomson heat can be at once found from the first
law of thermodynamics. If we call σ_t the heat absorbed per unit
volume per unit current density per unit transverse temperature
gradient per unit time, we have, on setting the total heats equal
to the work done by the E.M.F. :

$$\Delta\tau \frac{d}{d\tau}(iT) + \sigma_t \cdot ib \cdot \frac{iT}{\kappa_t} = e_t \cdot \frac{iT}{\kappa_t} \cdot ib,$$

or

$$\frac{iTb}{\kappa_t}\frac{d}{d\tau}(iT) + \sigma_t \frac{i^2bT}{\kappa_t} = \frac{i^2bT^2}{\kappa_t\tau},$$

or

$$\sigma_t + \frac{dT}{d\tau} = \frac{T}{\tau},$$

which may be written

$$\sigma_t = -\tau\frac{d}{d\tau}\left(\frac{T}{\tau}\right). \qquad \text{VI, 8.}$$

This is obviously the exact analog of the equation of the ordinary thermo-electric circuit

$$\sigma_A - \sigma_B = -\tau\frac{d}{d\tau}\left(\frac{P_{AB}}{\tau}\right).$$

Kelvin's proof of the necessity of the existence of a transverse
heating effect involved explicitly his axiom of the superposition
of heating effects, which amounts to the same thing as the assumption of the $\cos^2$ law. Since the $\cos^2$ law is not perfectly certain
it is interesting to inquire whether the necessity for the existence
of a transverse heating cannot be made to depend on some
demonstrable experimental fact in the same way that we saw the
existence of an internal Peltier heat depends only on the experi-
mentally established difference between $P_{\|m}$ and $P_{\perp m}$. Consider
the arrangement of crystal and isotropic metal of Figure 21. I
this is isothermal, the total heat generation when current passes
must vanish. But the effects at the interfaces A_1A_2 and D_1D
mutually cancel, and if there are lateral effects, the effect on A_1B
is cancelled by that on A_2B_2, and that on C_1D_1 by that on C_2D_2

all this by considerations of symmetry. Hence the total heating effects at the surfaces B_1C_1, B_2C_2, and B_1C_2 must together vanish. But the effect on B_1C_1 is equal to that on B_2C_2 by symmetry. Hence if we can accept as an experimental fact that the heat at the interface B_1C_2 is different from zero, there must be a compensating non-vanishing effect at the transverse faces. It seems most natural to suppose that there is an effect on B_1C_2 because of the change of orientation on crossing the surface, and we do in

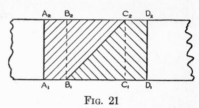

Fig. 21

fact know that there is such an effect. But it would seem that special measurement would be necessary to establish this as a primary experimental fact, and this would not be an especially easy sort of measurement to make because it would demand large crystals. I do not see any way of proving the necessity of the existence of a transverse heat from the mere experimental fact that a couple composed of rods of different orientations has a net E.M.F., but some additional independent experimental fact seems to be necessary.

We are now in a position to obtain the general expressions for the heat developed at an interface of any orientation when current flowing in any direction in the crystal crosses the interface into the isotropic metal. The situation is more complicated here than in the cases we have already considered. We have seen that if the current flow in the crystal is either parallel or perpendicular to the axis, the heat at the interface is independent of the orientation of the interface, so that in this case only one parameter is needed to specify the heat, namely, the angle between current flow and axis. But in general this is not true, and the interfacial heat depends on the angle between current flow and crystal axis and on the difference of orientation between the axis and the normal to the surface. In general two angles would be required to fix this latter orientation, but it is easy to see that because of rotational symmetry the two angles reduce to one. This parameter is obtained by taking the intersection of the interface with the plane of the axis and the length of the rod, and drawing the per-

pendicular to the intersection, or, what is the same thing, project-
ing the normal to the interface onto the plane of the axis and
length.   The angle between the axis and the perpendicular may
be taken as the second parameter.   Call θ the angle between current flow and axis, and α the angle between axis and the projected
normal to the interface.   Then the interfacial heat may be written $P(\theta, \alpha)$, where the subscript m, denoting the isotropic metal,
is suppressed, as being sufficiently well understood.   Then the
result that we have already found may be expressed in the form
that $P(0°, \alpha)$ and $P(90°, \alpha)$ are independent of α.

To obtain the general relation, consider a bar of unit square
section with the axis lying in the plane of one of the sides, as

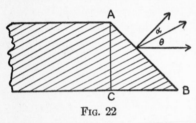

FIG. 22

shown in Figure 22.   The axis
makes an angle θ with the length,
which is the direction of current
flow.   The projection of the interface onto the plane containing
the axis is AB, and the projected
normal makes an angle α with
the axis.   The sign convention
with regard to these angles is obvious enough from the figure.
One can see at once that these parameters are sufficient by imag-
ining the interface to rock on the line AB as axis.   Equal triangles are described on the two bounding surfaces of the square
perpendicular to the paper, and on these triangles there are surface lateral heats, but these heats are equal and opposite by
symmetry, and cancel.   It is therefore sufficient to consider only
the case where the interface is perpendicular to the plane of the
paper.   We now have the fact, demanded by the second law, that
the total heat absorbed when the current passes from crystal to
isotropic metal is independent of the orientation of the interface.
One possible interface is AC; in this case there are no other net
heating effects.   When the interface is AB, there is a heating at
the interface, and a lateral heat at BC.   The sum of these must
equal the heat on AC.   The heat on AC is $P(\theta, -\theta)$, the lateral
heat on CB is $T(\theta) \tan(\alpha + \theta)$, and the heat on AB is $P(\theta, \alpha)$
Hence,

$$P(\theta, \alpha) + T(\theta) \tan(\alpha + \theta) = P(\theta, -\theta).$$

This equation is independent of any assumption about the form of T. Assuming Kelvin's relations, we have:

$$T(\theta) = (P_\parallel - P_\perp) \cos \theta \sin \theta,$$

and

$$P(\theta, -\theta) = P_\parallel \cos^2 \theta + P_\perp \sin^2 \theta.$$

Substituting and solving,

$$P(\theta, \alpha) = \frac{P_\parallel [\cos^2 \theta - \sin^2 \theta - 2 \tan \alpha \sin \theta \cos \theta] + P_\perp \left[2 \sin^2 \theta - \tan \alpha \left(\dfrac{\sin^3 \theta}{\cos \theta} - \cos \theta \sin \theta \right) \right]}{1 - \tan \alpha \tan \theta},$$

VI, 9.

the desired relation. One may immediately verify that when $\theta = 0°$ or $90°$, $P(\theta, \alpha)$ is independent of α, and reduces to the proper known value.

If one cares to take the trouble, it is now possible to verify Kelvin's axiom by direct substitution, using any method of resolving the current into components. The work is long and is not worth reproducing here.

We may also now get a general expression for the internal Peltier heat absorbed when the direction of current flow changes from an angle θ_1 with the axis to an angle θ_2, the density of current being unaltered after change of direction. Call this internal

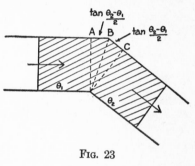

Fig. 23

Peltier heat $I(\theta_1, \theta_2)$. The calculation is at once obvious from Figure 23. The total heat absorbed at the entrance and exit interfaces, at the bend, and the lateral heats on the two surfaces AB and BC is zero. Hence,

$$- P(\theta_1, -\theta_1) + P(\theta_2, -\theta_2) + I(\theta_1, \theta_2)$$
$$+ \tan \frac{\theta_2 - \theta_1}{2} [T(\theta_1) + T(\theta_2)] = 0.$$

The known values for P and T may be substituted in this equation, which gives, on solving for I,

$$I(\theta_1, \theta_2) = P_\parallel (\cos^2 \theta_1 - \cos^2 \theta_2) + P_\perp (\sin^2 \theta_1 - \sin^2 \theta_2)$$
$$- (P_\parallel - P_\perp)(\cos \theta_1 \sin \theta_1 + \cos \theta_2 \sin \theta_2) \tan \frac{\theta_2 - \theta_1}{2}. \quad \text{VI, 10.}$$

It is particularly to be noted that the total internal heat in changing direction at once from θ_1 to θ_2 is not the sum of the heats in changing first from θ_1 to θ_3 and then from θ_3 to θ_2. This may be verified easily by putting $\theta_1 = 0$, $\theta_2 = 90°$, $\theta_3 = 45°$. The obvious explanation is that the complete operation of getting from θ_1 to θ_2 by two steps has involved non-cancelling surface lateral heats as well as the internal heats, as is indeed suggested by Figure 23.

We next consider other effects in crystals, such as the Volta effect and the heats of vaporization of electrons. The methods and formulas already developed may be applied, remembering the fundamental fact that there can be no jump of potential at

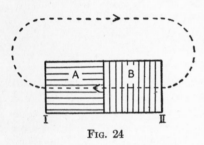

FIG. 24

an interface between two different orientations of the same crystal, which would mean, in the notation of Chapter IV that $S_{\theta_1\theta_2} = 0$. One expects in general Volta differences between different faces of the same crystal, and therefore different electron vapor densities in equilibrium with different faces, different thermionic emission from different faces, different heats of evaporation, and different surface heats.

We may obtain one relation immediately by applying formula IV, 9, identifying the two metals A and B with two orientations of the same crystal, as in Figure 24. This gives:

$$\eta_{\rho\mathrm{I}} - \eta_{\rho\mathrm{II}} = e(P_{\parallel\perp} - V_{\mathrm{I,II}}), \qquad \text{VI, 11.}$$

where I and II denote the two surfaces indicated. This equation corresponds to a continuous cycle, electricity being carried straight through the metal as indicated by the arrow. The experimental fact that $P_{\parallel\perp} \neq 0$ shows that all the other quantities in this equation cannot be identically zero, and that therefore there are real differences at different faces. Now it is most important to notice that the latent heat at constant surface charge, η_ρ, must depend on the direction of motion of electricity in the metal as it is brought up to the surface, as inspection of

Figure 25 shows at once. For if the electron is brought up at an angle, and then its direction of motion changed to normal to the surface, the internal Peltier heat corresponding to the change of direction must be merged in the heat of vaporization in the limit when the change of direction takes place at the surface itself.

The dependence of η_ρ on the direction of motion of the electron just below the surface can be found at once from formula 10 for the internal Peltier heat; it is not worth while to write out an explicit formula. The situation is further complicated by the fact that there are other compensating developments of heat in the body of the metal corresponding to terms of the type $\partial i_x/\partial y$ when the direction of approach to the surface changes, so that equation 10

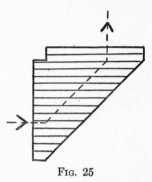

Fig. 25

becomes complicated. If, however, the term $P_{\parallel\perp}$ is generalized to include *all* the internal heating effects for any particular method of transporting the current through the crystal from one surface to another, equation 11 remains valid, the $\eta'_\rho S$ and the P being complicated functions.

These considerations do not apply to the heat of vaporization, η, which corresponds to vaporization in the isolated system, the electric charge in the vapor being compensated by the charge left behind on the surface. For, obviously, the electrons constituting the vapor may be thought of as originating in the surface, so that it is not pertinent to speak of the direction of approach of the electron to the surface in the metal. Since we have the general relation $\eta = \eta_\rho - eP_S$, we see at once that the surface heat of charging is a function of the direction of electron approach such as to exactly compensate for the corresponding term in η_ρ.

We have thus far confined our attention almost exclusively to linear currents carried in long slender crystal rods. There is evidently a much more general problem, namely, the heating effects in a massive crystal with any distribution of current and any temperature distribution. This general problem has been solved, as already stated, by Ehrenfest and Rutgers.[10] Their solution is a development in more elegant mathematical form of the method of Kelvin. Voigt, in his book "Krystallphysik," also gives a treatment which purports to be a generalization of Kelvin, but he has left out important terms, so that the net E.M.F. around a complete thermo-circuit is zero according to his equations. In the following I reproduce the formulation of Ehrenfest and Rutgers, first written out explicitly in Cartesian coördinates for crystals, particularizing the constants so as to correspond to the rotational symmetry shown by all metals, and discuss this formulation briefly, and then, by way of completeness, I reproduce their most general formulas in tensor form for any non-isotropic non-homogeneous material, which must include crystals as a special case.

We take the X axis of coördinates along the principal axis of the crystal; the Y and Z axes are any set at right angles, their precise orientation being a matter of indifference because of rotational symmetry for thermo-electric phenomena. The state of affairs is assumed to be steady, so that the current satisfies the condition:

$$\text{Div } i \equiv \frac{\partial i_x}{\partial x} + \frac{\partial i_y}{\partial y} + \frac{\partial i_z}{\partial z} = 0. \qquad \text{VI, 12.}$$

In the body of the crystal there is a reversible absorption of heat equal to ω per unit volume per unit quantity of electricity, and ω satisfies the equation:

$$\frac{\omega}{\tau} = \frac{\partial}{\partial x}\left[i_x S_\| + (i_y + i_z)(S_\perp - S_\|)\right] + \frac{\partial}{\partial y}\left[i_x(S_\| - S_\perp) + i_y S_\perp\right]$$

$$+ \frac{\partial}{\partial z}\left[i_x(S_\| - S_\perp) + i_z S_\perp\right], \qquad \text{VI, 13.}$$

where $\qquad S_\| = \int_0^\tau \frac{\sigma_\|}{\tau}\, d\tau \quad$ and $\quad S_\perp = \int_0^\tau \frac{\sigma_\perp}{\tau}\, d\tau.$

At an interface between two media (1) and (2), with direction cosines n_x, n_y, n_z of the normal pointing *into* the region (1), there is a reversible absorption of heat per unit surface of

$$\frac{\omega}{\tau} = n_x\left[i_x S_\| + (i_y + i_z)(S_\perp - S_\|)\right] + n_y\left[i_x(S_\| - S_\perp) + i_y S_\perp\right]$$

$$+ n_z\left[i_x(S_\| - S_\perp) + i_z S_\perp\right]. \qquad \text{VI, 14.}$$

This expression is obtained in the conventional way from the expression for the generation of heat per unit volume by proceeding to the limit.

The driving e.m.f. has the components:

$$\left.\begin{array}{l}
(\text{e.m.f.})_{dx} = -\dfrac{\partial \tau}{\partial x} S_\parallel - \left(\dfrac{\partial \tau}{\partial y} + \dfrac{\partial \tau}{\partial z}\right)(S_\perp - S_\parallel) - \dfrac{\partial R}{\partial x} \\[2ex]
(\text{e.m.f.})_{dy} = -\dfrac{\partial \tau}{\partial x}(S_\parallel - S_\perp) - \dfrac{\partial \tau}{\partial y} S_\perp \qquad\quad - \dfrac{\partial R}{\partial y} \\[2ex]
(\text{e.m.f.})_{dz} = -\dfrac{\partial \tau}{\partial x}(S_\parallel - S_\perp) - \dfrac{\partial \tau}{\partial z} S_\perp \qquad\quad - \dfrac{\partial R}{\partial z}
\end{array}\right\} \quad \text{VI, 15.}$$

Here R is an arbitrary function of temperature, which is in general different for different materials. The difference of R at the interface between two different media gives the undeterminable Volta jump of potential at the interface.

The general correctness of these equations may be checked by showing that they satisfy the first and second laws of thermodynamics. We notice as a preliminary that because of the condition $\text{Div}\, i = 0$ the current flows in closed loops inside the conductor. The first law may now be expressed in the form that the net work done by $(\text{e.m.f.})_w$ in any closed current circuit is equal to the total heat absorbed. But we have already shown that the integral around any closed current circuit of the work done by $(\text{e.m.f.})_w$ is equal to the integral around the same circuit of $i(\text{e.m.f.})_d$, so that the first law demands that the net heat absorption in any closed circuit be equal to the integral around the circuit of $i(\text{e.m.f.})_d$. The second law demands, since the processes are reversible, that the total change of entropy vanish. The conductor itself is in a steady state, so that the entropy of the reservoirs which supply the conductor must be constant, or $\dfrac{\omega}{\tau}$ integrated over the entire conductor must vanish.

The proof that these two conditions are satisfied is immediate, by simple substitution, each condition leading to an identity. It is obvious that the integral around the circuit of the terms in R vanishes because the integral of i over the cross section of a tube of current flow is constant, and R returns to its initial value. The second law is seen to be satisfied at once because by Green's theorem the volume integral transforms into the negative over the bounding surface of the contribution given by equation 14 for the interface.

It is also easy to see by applying the formulas to simple cases of rods cut along the axis and current flowing along the rod that the formulas already given are obtained. The various internal heats are a consequence of the non-vanishing of terms such as $\partial i_x/\partial x$ or $\partial i_x/\partial y$ in regions at constant temperature where the direction of current flow changes or where the current strength varies perpendicularly to the direction of flow.

It is important to notice that one cannot speak in the general case of a convection of thermal energy by the entire current, for in general the direction of flow of thermal energy is not the same as the direction of flow of electrical current. Of course the same is true of the stream of convected entropy, a point especially insisted on by Ehrenfest and Rutgers. One may, however, speak of a definite convection of thermal energy by the components of current parallel and perpendicular to the axis. These components have, therefore, a certain degree of physical reality, which is not surprising when one considers the finite expenditure of energy required merely to change the direction of motion of an electron.

It is interesting to write out the equations for the specially simple case of a homogeneous isotropic conductor. For this

$$S_{\parallel} \equiv S_{\perp} \equiv S = \int_0^{\tau} \frac{\sigma}{\tau}\, d\tau. \qquad \text{VI, 16.}$$

Absorption of heat per unit volume,

$$\omega = \tau \, \text{Div} \, (iS). \qquad \text{VI, 17.}$$

At an interface : $\omega = \tau[S_1 i_1 \cdot n - S_2 i_2 \cdot n], \qquad \text{VI, 18.}$

and $(\text{e.m.f.})_d = - \, S \, \text{Grad} \, \tau - \text{Grad} \, R. \qquad \text{VI, 19.}$

Finally, for the sake of completeness, I reproduce the equations of Ehrenfest and Rutgers for any temperature distribution in any non-homogeneous non-isotropic body, with, however, a different sign convention, a heat absorbed by the conductor being here taken as positive instead of negative. We take as the three axes x_1, x_2, x_3, and suppress the summation signs when there are two equal subscripts, as is usual in tensor analysis. Then the condition for steady current is:

$$\frac{\partial i_\alpha}{\partial x_\alpha} = 0, \quad \alpha = 1, 2, 3. \qquad \text{VI, 20.}$$

The reversible generation of heat per unit volume per unit quantity is:

$$\omega = \tau \frac{\partial}{\partial x_\beta} (i_\alpha S_{\alpha\beta}), \qquad \text{VI, 21.}$$

where $S_{\alpha\beta}$ are coefficients, functions of the nature of the material and the temperature, the generalizations of $S_\parallel$ and $S_\perp - S_\parallel$ above. The reversible generation at an interface is:

$$\omega = \tau \left| n_\beta i_\alpha S_{\alpha\beta} \right|_{\text{med (1)}}^{\text{med (2)}}, \qquad \text{VI, 22.}$$

and, finally, $\qquad (\text{e.m.f.})_{d\alpha} = -\frac{\partial \tau}{\partial x_\beta} S_{\alpha\beta} - \frac{\partial R}{\partial x_\alpha}. \qquad \text{VI, 23.}$

It should be said that Ehrenfest and Rutgers do not speak of a " driving e.m.f.," but this is my transcription into my language of their notation.

None of these sets of equations are sufficient to completely solve the problem; we require also the equations of heat conduction and the equations giving current flow in terms of potential gradient, $(\text{e.m.f.})_d$, and the various coefficients of resistance. The way in which these other equations are to be utilized in obtaining the complete solution has been indicated in connection with the simple problems of linear flow.

CHAPTER VII

THE TRANSVERSE GALVANOMAGNETIC AND THERMOMAGNETIC PHENOMENA

It is well known that if a homogeneous isotropic substance is subject to a magnetic field and at the same time carries a current of electricity or a flow of heat, there will be certain redistributions brought about in the equipotential and isothermal surfaces. Four of these effects are transverse; I shall deduce certain relations between these four transverse effects by reasoning of a thermodynamic or other general character.

First, it will be well to review the definition of the effects. We suppose the homogeneous isotropic metal is in the form of a longitudinal rod or plate of rectangular section, of breadth b and thickness d. A uniform magnetic field of strength H is supposed in all cases to be acting perpendicular to the face of the plate, that is, perpendicular to the dimension b and parallel to the dimension d. We shall allow an electric current or a heat current to flow lengthwise of the plate. The total electric current shall be I and its density i, where $ibd = I$, and the total heat current shall be W and its density w, where $wbd = W$. The effects are now defined as follows:

(1) The Hall effect. When electric current passes lengthwise, a transverse electric potential is set up, so that the current no longer flows perpendicular to the equipotential lines. The Hall coefficient R is defined by the equation $R = Ed/IH$, or

$$R = \frac{\text{Trans. Pot. Grad}}{iH}, \qquad \text{VII, 1.}$$

where E is the total difference of potential set up between opposite sides of the plate. The coefficient is taken as positive if the electric potential is raised on that side of the plate where the Amperean current generating the magnetic field has the same direction as the current i.

132

The transverse potential difference is to be thought of as the result of a transverse E.M.F. which appears in the body of the plate when current flows perpendicular to the magnetic field. Since no transverse current flows in the steady state, we may apply Ohm's law and obtain $(\text{e.m.f.})_d$ = Trans. Pot. Grad. A metal exhibiting the Hall phenomenon is therefore the seat of a uniformly distributed $(\text{e.m.f.})_d$. But we have already seen that the integral around a complete circuit of $(\text{e.m.f.})_w$ is equal to the corresponding integral of $(\text{e.m.f.})_d$, and since in this case there are no surfaces of discontinuity, as in the thermo-electric case, and we must suppose that the seat of the $(\text{e.m.f.})_w$ must be the body of the plate and uniformly distributed there, we must have $(\text{e.m.f.})_d = (\text{e.m.f.})_w$ at every point. That is, the distinction between the two kinds of e.m.f. vanishes for this phenomenon, and we may speak simply of the Hall e.m.f., of amount equal to the transverse potential gradient $= iRH$.

(2) The Ettingshausen effect. When electric current flows lengthwise of the plate, a transverse temperature difference is generated, the plate being thermally isolated from its surroundings. The Ettingshausen coefficient P is defined by the equation $P = \Delta\tau \times d/IH$

or
$$P = \frac{\text{Trans. Temp. Grad}}{iH}, \qquad \text{VII, 2.}$$

where $\Delta\tau$ is the total difference of temperature between opposite sides of the plate. P is taken as positive if the temperature rises on that side of the plate where the Amperean current generating the magnetic field and the longitudinal electric current i have the same direction.

(3) The Nernst effect. If a heat current flows lengthwise of the plate, a transverse electric potential difference is generated. The conventional Nernst coefficient is denoted by Q and is defined by the equation $Q = E\kappa d/WH$, or

$$Q = \frac{\kappa \times \text{Trans. Pot. Grad}}{wH}, \qquad \text{VII, 3.}$$

where κ is the thermal conductivity. There is thus a lack of symmetry between the definition of Q and the definitions of R and P.

It is therefore convenient to introduce an altered Nernst coefficient, Q', defined by $\kappa Q' = Q$. We now have

$$Q' = \frac{\text{Trans. Pot. Grad}}{wH}, \qquad \text{VII, 4.}$$

completely analogous to the definitions of R and P. The signs of Q and Q' are to be taken as positive if the potential is increased on that side of the plate where the Amperean current generating the magnetic field and the heat current have the same direction. This transverse potential gradient is the result of a uniformly distributed transverse e.m.f., exactly as in the case of the Hall phenomenon, there being no distinction between $(\text{e.m.f.})_w$ and $(\text{e.m.f.})_d$.

(4) The Righi-Leduc effect. If a heat current flows lengthwise of the plate, a transverse temperature difference is set up when the plate is thermally isolated laterally from its surroundings. The Righi-Leduc coefficient, S, is defined by the equation $S = \Delta \tau \times \kappa d / WH$

or $$S = \frac{\kappa \times \text{Trans. Temp. Grad}}{wH}. \qquad \text{VII, 5.}$$

As for the Nernst coefficient, it is convenient to introduce a modified Righi-Leduc coefficient, S', defined by $\kappa S' = S$, or

$$S' = \frac{\text{Trans. Temp. Grad}}{wH}. \qquad \text{VII, 6.}$$

The signs of S and S' are positive by convention if the temperature is raised on that side of the plate where the Amperean current generating the magnetic field and the longitudinal heat current have the same direction.

These four effects involve a transverse potential difference or difference of temperature which is permanently maintained as long as the longitudinal electric or thermal current continues to flow. The potential difference or the difference of temperature may therefore be made the source of a permanent supply of energy, either by tapping across the two sides of the plate and using it like a battery, or by connecting the two sides through a thermodynamic engine, and using the two sides as thermal source and

sink. We may apply the first law of thermodynamics in asking
what is the source of the permanent output of energy, and we
may apply the second law if the effects are reversible.

Consider first the application of the first law to the Hall phenomenon : what is the source of the energy drawn from the system when a transverse current is allowed to flow between the sides
of the plate, delivering energy to an external electro-magnetic
engine? Since current flow in the steady state is continuous, the
external transverse flow must be completed by an equal transverse flow in the body of the metal. Call this interior transverse
current I_t, and the longitudinal current I_l. The energy which I_t
takes from the system in unit time is the product of current and
transverse potential difference, or $I_t R I_l H/d$. But when I_t flows,
it is itself subject to the Hall phenomenon, and sets up a potential difference at right angles to itself, that is, parallel to the
original current, of amount $R I_t H/d$. If the original current is
maintained constant, as we suppose it is, the E.M.F. that drives
it must do an additional amount of work against this induced
longitudinal potential difference of $I_l R I_t H/d$. But this is numerically exactly the energy extracted by the transverse current,
and inspection shows that the signs are the same. The Hall phenomenon therefore automatically acts as its own source of energy,
the current by which energy is extracted from the system setting
up such a potential difference in the direction of the primary current as to automatically extract from the primary source of
energy the requisite additional energy.

Next consider the Ettingshausen temperature difference between opposite sides of the plate ; we must discuss in the first
place what the nature of this temperature difference is. Perhaps
the most natural point of view is that, since one side of the plate
is maintained continuously hot and the other side cold, there is a
continuous flow of heat by thermal conduction in the plate from
hot to cold. But thermal conduction is essentially irreversible,
so that according to this point of view the Ettingshausen phenomenon is essentially irreversible. If this point of view is correct,
we can now find at once a necessary connection between the
Ettingshausen and the Nernst effects. The continuous dissipation of energy by irreversible heat conduction demands a contin-

uous increase of the entropy of the entire universe, and this can mean, under these conditions, only a continual rise of temperature of the entire plate. The energy which produces this temperature rise must come from the primary current. The primary current is able to deliver this energy because the transverse thermal conduction current produces by the Nernst effect a longitudinal E.M.F. for the primary electric current to work against. The transverse temperature difference is $\Delta \tau = PI_lH/d$. The transverse heat flow per unit length is $W_t = \kappa d \, \Delta \tau / b$. The longitudinal E.M.F. per unit length produced by the transverse heat flow W_t is $QW_tH/\kappa d$, and inspection of the signs shows that if both P and Q are positive, this e.m.f. is in the direction of the primary current. The primary current therefore delivers in virtue of this e.m.f. an additional energy $- I_lQW_tH/\kappa d$. This energy is converted into heat, and results in an entropy rise per unit length of $- I_lQW_tH/\kappa \, d\tau$. But the entropy rise because of the irreversible heat conduction is $W_t \, \Delta \tau / \tau^2$, or $W_t PI_lH/d\tau^2$. Equating these two entropy changes gives

$$P = - \frac{Q}{\kappa} \tau = - Q'\tau.$$

The relation was probably first deduced by Lorentz, by an argument formally different from that presented above, and was reported by him to the Solvay Congress on Metallic Conduction in 1924.[17] It may be checked by experiment, and turns out to be exactly wrong. Numerically the two sides of the equation are equal within experimental error, but the sign is incorrect.

It appears, therefore, that the view that the Ettingshausen phenomenon is essentially irreversible cannot be correct. The view that this effect is essentially irreversible was also held by Voigt in his book " Krystallphysik," who states that since the transverse effects are essentially irreversible, it is impossible to apply to them such analysis as is necessary to determine the necessary symmetry relations in crystals. Voigt let the matter rest at that, without attempting to carry the matter further, as did Lorentz.

A diametrically opposite view of the nature of the Ettingshausen temperature difference therefore seems to be demanded.

The conclusions to be deduced from such a view were presented by me, also to the Solvay Congress in 1924. This work was done independently of Lorentz's; it is a curious example of scientific coincidence that a phenomenon which had not been subject to thermodynamic analysis since its discovery forty years before should be independently attacked by two different persons within a few days of each other.

According to this view the temperature difference between the sides of the plate does not result in a thermal conduction current through the plate, but the temperature difference is permanently maintained with no thermal flow. The plate is the seat of a " thermo-motive force " exactly analogous to the electro-motive force of a battery. Just as the terminals of a battery on open circuit are maintained at a constant potential difference by the E.M.F. of the battery with no internal flow of electricity, so here the sides of the plate are maintained at a constant difference of temperature by the " T.M.F." within the plate, with no internal flow of heat. Just as an E.M.F. does work when current flows with it, so a T.M.F. does work when heat flows through it. But the expressions for work done by E.M.F. and T.M.F. are not exactly analogous, because heat is a form of energy by itself, whereas electricity is not. A T.M.F. does work when a thermal current flows through it by actually increasing the magnitude of the thermal current, the thermal current leaving being greater than that entering by the work done. Furthermore, a heat current can do work only when it flows through a difference of temperature, so that the T.M.F. does work primarily by maintaining a temperature difference $\Delta\tau$ and then the heat current W receives from it the work $W\dfrac{\Delta\tau}{\tau}$.

Apply this picture to the Ettingshausen phenomenon. Extract work from the temperature difference between the two sides of the plate by using them as source and sink of a heat engine. Let a heat current W_t flow from the hot side per unit length. The heat engine extracts from it the energy $W_t\dfrac{\Delta\tau}{\tau}$. A heat current of magnitude $W_t\left(1 - \dfrac{\Delta\tau}{\tau}\right)$ enters the cold side of the plate, and flows transversely in the plate, *against* the transverse temperature difference, being augmented as it flows by the transverse T.M.F., until at emergence at the hot side it is built up again to the value W_t. This heat flow in the plate is the source of a longitudinal E.M.F. by the Nernst phenomenon, exactly as in the preceding argument, but now, since the heat flow in the plate is from cold to hot, instead of from hot to cold, the longitudinal E.M.F. is in the opposite direction, so that now energy is extracted from the longitudinal current, instead of delivered to it, and it is certain that the sign, at least, must agree with experiment.

The actual magnitudes of the effects may be calculated as before. It is obvious that in computing the longitudinal E.M.F. the transverse heat current may be treated as constant to the order of terms significant. The longitudinal E.M.F. per unit length is $QW_t H/\kappa d$, and the work done against this by the longitudinal current is $I_e QW_t H/\kappa d$. The work extracted by the transverse heat current is $W_t \dfrac{\Delta \tau}{\tau} = W_t PI_t H/d\tau$. Equating these gives:

$$P = \frac{Q}{\kappa} \tau = Q'\tau. \qquad \text{VII, 7.}$$

This is exactly the same relation as obtained before except for the sign, and this is checked by experiment, within error. The idea of a thermo-motive force analogous to an electro-motive force therefore seems to be justified. In the printed report of the Solvay Congress, issued several years after the meeting of the Congress, Lorentz added a discussion in which he recognized and accepted the necessity for the concept of thermo-motive force as a correct description of the Ettingshausen phenomenon.

There is a formal analogy between the Ettingshausen phenomenon and the transverse temperature difference set up in a crystal bar inclined to the axis when longitudinal current flows. In fact, the analogy is rather far reaching, for the Hall effect and the Righi-Leduc effects have their analogs in the fact that in a crystal electric flow or thermal flow is not perpendicular to the equipotential or isothermal surfaces, and the Nernst effect has its analog in the transverse Thomson effect in crystals. The analogy is only formal, however, for in the crystal bar the temperature difference is accompanied by an internal flow of heat from hot to cold, and in fact the magnitude of the transverse temperature difference in crystals may be computed by assuming complete irreversibility. The signs of the effects are therefore opposite in the two cases, and the obliquely cut crystal bar is not the seat of a T.M.F. The mechanisms in the two cases must therefore be quite different.

Returning now to the argument above, the application of the first law to the other two effects, the Nernst and the Righi-Leduc effects, yields no new relations. For consider first the Nernst effect. Here a longitudinal heat current produces a transverse potential difference, which may be made to deliver energy by allowing a transverse electric current to flow. But this transverse electric current sets up a longitudinal T.M.F. by the Ettingshausen phenomenon, and the primary heat current flowing against this T.M.F. delivers an additional amount of energy exactly equal to that extracted by the transverse electric current. Detailed analysis results in the same relation between P and Q as that deduced already.

Similar analysis applies to the Righi-Leduc effect. A longitudinal heat current produces a transverse temperature difference, which may be made to deliver energy externally by allowing a transverse heat current to flow. But this transverse heat current itself produces by the Righi-Leduc effect a longitudinal temperature difference in virtue of which the longitudinal heat current delivers just the requisite additional energy. The Righi-Leduc phenomenon therefore supplies its own source of energy, just as did the Hall phenomenon. It is important to notice again that the concept of thermo-motive force is necessary. The Righi-Leduc temperature difference is the manifestation of an internal T.M.F. which maintains a permanent temperature difference in the metal with no resulting heat flow. The Righi-Leduc phenomena are perfectly reversible; if this were not the case, there would be an inconsistency of sign.

Having now made highly probable that the four transverse effects are completely reversible, it is legitimate to apply the second law. The situation is complicated by the coexistence of irreversible phenomena, for the continual action of a battery is needed to drive the longitudinal current against the resistance of the plate, or if the longitudinal current is thermal, energy must be continually supplied to compensate for the dissipation of energy always accompanying thermal conduction. The situation is therefore much like that with respect to thermo-electric phenomena, but it is simpler, for there is only one primary mechanism of dissipation instead of two, and one might expect to be able to make the irreversible aspects vanishing small compared with the reversible aspects by a proper choice of the dimensions of the circuit. This may be easily shown to be possible for the Hall phenomenon, for example. Imagine the plate carrying the longitudinal current to be bent into the shape of a complete toroid, and placed in a magnetic field perpendicular to its plane. Let there be a current I flowing circumferentially in the toroid, without any battery to drive it, maintained by the energy of self-induction $\frac{1}{2} L I^2$, and gradually dying down as the $\frac{1}{2} L I^2$ energy is frittered away in overcoming the resistance. The outer and inner circumferences of the toroid are at a difference of potential in virtue of the Hall effect, and by connecting these circumferences they may be treated like the terminals of a battery, and energy taken out of the system when current flows radially in the toroid. The source of this energy is also $\frac{1}{2} L I^2$ energy. If the linear dimensions of the circuit are all increased in the same ratio, L increases as the linear dimensions and the resistance decreases in the same ratio, so that by suitably choosing the dimensions the rate of dissipation of the energy of self-induction may be made as slow as we please. Then having chosen the dimensions, I may be decreased; the Joulean dissipation goes down as I^2 and the Hall E.M.F. as I, so that by decreasing I the ratio of Joulean dissipation to E.M.F. may be made as small as we please. In the limit we have a system capable of maintaining itself indefinitely, yielding energy to the exterior only when radial current is drawn against the Hall E.M.F. The Joulean dissipation by the radial current offers no more difficulty for thermodynamic analysis than the internal resistance of an ordinary battery for the conventional thermodynamic analysis of its action. Instead, however, of all this juggling with dimensions, it would be much simpler to let the irreversible effects rise to their full value and simply add to the entropy changes accompanying the reversible processes the entropy changes contributed by the irreversible effects, treating these as characteristic of the irreversible processes and independent of the reversible processes. Terms will thus be obtained which will cancel from both sides of the equations, and we will be left with results which might have been obtained in the beginning by applying the second law only to the reversible phenomena, neglecting the irreversible aspects. The situation is exactly the same as that with regard to the alternative argument for deducing the thermo-electric equations given on page 55.

Given now the plate of the conventional Hall effect, taken as of unit length; we shall suppose that the longitudinal current flows indefinitely except as it may deliver energy when it is tapped by a transverse current, just as if the circuit were made of a superconducting material. The transverse E.M.F. is RIH/d, and the system acts like a battery. It is an experimental fact that R is a function of temperature, so that the E.M.F. of this battery is a function of temperature, and the conventional thermodynamic analysis may be at once applied, resulting in Helmholtz's relation between temperature derivative of E.M.F. and heat necessary to maintain the battery isothermal during operation. However, the analysis is so simple that it will pay to reproduce it in full. Let a quantity of electricity δq_e flow transversely, where the round δ is used to avoid confusion with the depth of the plate. The work done is $\delta W = \delta q_e \times$ E.M.F. $= \delta q_e RIH/d$. With our set-up, the only way by which work may be given to the surroundings is by the passage of transverse current, so that this is the complete expression for δW. As variables fixing the condition of the system choose temperature, τ, and q_e, transverse quantity of electricity. The first law gives:

$$\delta Q = \left(\frac{\partial E}{\partial \tau}\right)_{q_e} \delta \tau + \left(\frac{\partial E}{\partial q_e}\right)_{\tau} \delta q_e + \left(\frac{RIH}{d}\right)\delta q_e.$$

Now form $\delta S = \delta Q/\tau$ and write the condition that δS be a perfect differential by equating the cross derivatives of the coefficients of $\delta\tau$ and δq_e. This gives:

$$\left(\frac{\partial Q}{\partial q_e}\right)_\tau = \tau \frac{H}{d}\left(\frac{\partial(RI)}{\partial\tau}\right)_{q_e}, \qquad \text{VII, 8.}$$

neglecting the thermal expansion of the toroid, which would introduce only ordinary effects associated with thermal expansion. In circuits with appreciable thermal expansion, there is an E.M.F. in the circuit in virtue of the changing self-induction when temperature changes; such effects are in addition to those considered here. We may write equation 8 in terms of specific quantities. Q', the absorption of heat per unit volume, is equal to Q/bd; q'_e, the density of transverse flow, is equal to q_e/d; and $i = I/bd$. Whence

$$\left(\frac{\partial Q'}{\partial q'_e}\right)_\tau = \tau H \left(\frac{\partial(Ri)}{\partial\tau}\right)_{q'_e}. \qquad \text{VII, 9.}$$

This equation appears to demand an inflow of heat in order to maintain temperature constant when transverse current is allowed to flow. It is linear in both longitudinal and transverse flow, so that the heat reverses sign when either current reverses. For the metal bismuth, R is known to change by the fraction 0.004 of itself for one degree rise of temperature. Calculation shows that with so large a temperature derivative of R the thermal effect demanded by equation 9 should be easily demonstrable for bismuth, neglecting the totally unknown term $\frac{\partial i}{\partial\tau}$. I accordingly set up an experiment with bismuth to detect this new heating effect. Some of the details of this experiment will be found in *Phys. Rev.* 39, 707, 1932. There were various difficulties, but the final result was that no effect exists of more than $\frac{1}{10}$ of that calculated from the temperature derivative of R. By the time the experiment was completed I was, however, entirely reconciled to this result because in the meantime two arguments had presented themselves which showed that the effect should vanish.

The first argument involves the vector character of the current.

Imagine the plate in the form of a symmetrical cross, the arms being of unit breadth and thickness. Let the primary longitudinal current flow in the horizontal arm, and let the Hall E.M.F. be tapped off by the vertical arms. Further, allow the transverse current to be the same in magnitude as the longitudinal current. The two currents combine vectorially in the center of the cross to a single current flowing approximately along the diagonal of the central square, as suggested in Figure 26. Now the seat of the heating effect must, of course, be connected somehow with the central square. But in the interior of the square we have merely a simple current flowing in a magnetic field, which was the original situation before the transverse current was started, and which by hypothesis and experiment is without heating effect. Therefore if there is a

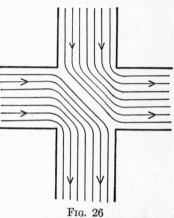

Fig. 26

heating effect, it must be around the periphery of the square, where the direction of current flow changes rapidly, something after the fashion of the internal Peltier heat of crystals. But examination shows that this is not possible from symmetry considerations, the contributions by elements in the right-hand lower diagonal being exactly cancelled by corresponding elements in the upper left-hand diagonal. Hence the net heating effect must vanish.

The second argument is derived from the symmetry of the longitudinal and transverse currents. Equation 9, written as an equation for absorption of heat, Q'', per unit volume per unit time, becomes:

$$\left(\frac{\partial Q''}{\partial i_t}\right)_\tau = \tau H \frac{\partial}{\partial \tau}(i_e R), \qquad \text{VII, 10.}$$

where i_t is transverse current density, and i_e longitudinal current density. But now Figure 26 is obviously symmetrical in i_t and i_e, and so the heat absorbed should be unchanged if the notation, longitudinal and transverse, is inverted.   But the original relation of i_l and i_t corresponds to "a" of Figure 27, and the inverted

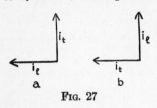

relation to "b" of the same figure. But now if i_t of Figure 27 b is brought into coincidence with i_t of Figure 27 a by rotation through 90°, the i_l is reversed, which would demand a reversal of the heating effect.   But the only quantity equal to its own negative is zero, so that again the heating effect must vanish.   We must have therefore

Fig. 27

$$\frac{\partial(iR)}{\partial \tau} = 0, \qquad\qquad \text{VII, 11.}$$

or

$$\frac{1}{i}\left(\frac{\partial i}{\partial \tau}\right)_{q_e} = -\frac{1}{R}\left(\frac{\partial R}{\partial \tau}\right)_{q_e} \neq 0. \qquad\qquad \text{VII, 12.}$$

This equation demands that the current in the system changes when temperature changes, no work being delivered by the system during the change of temperature, as indicated by the subscript of the partial derivative.   This means the existence of an entirely new kind of E.M.F., an E.M.F. in a circuit carrying a current when the temperature changes, the circuit being isolated from its surroundings except for the heat flow necessary to change the temperature.   Numerically, the magnitude of this E.M.F. cannot be negligibly small, since $\frac{1}{R}\frac{dR}{d\tau}$ may be as large as 0.004.

We may get a suggestive expression for this new E.M.F. by supposing that to a first approximation the work done by this E.M.F. on the current is at the expense of the energy of self-induction of the circuit, neglecting for the present any interaction between the energy of self-induction and the thermal energy of the conductor.   In order to get the right dimensional relations we may again think of our specimen in the form of a toroid, and the E.M.F. as an E.M.F. per unit length of the circumference of the toroid.   The work done by this E.M.F. in unit length is at the expense of the $\frac{1}{2} LI^2$ energy, where now L is the self-induction per unit length. We then have at once,

$$\frac{d}{dt}(\tfrac{1}{2} LI^2) = I \times \text{e.m.f.},$$

or
$$\text{e.m.f.} = L \frac{dI}{dt} = L \frac{dI}{d\tau} \frac{d\tau}{dt}.$$

But
$$\frac{1}{I}\left(\frac{\partial I}{\partial \tau}\right) = \frac{1}{i}\left(\frac{\partial i}{\partial \tau}\right), \quad \text{and} \quad \frac{\partial I}{\partial \tau} = -I \frac{1}{R}\frac{\partial R}{\partial \tau},$$

so that finally,
$$\text{e.m.f.} = -IL \frac{1}{R}\frac{\partial R}{\partial \tau}\frac{d\tau}{dt}. \qquad \text{VII, 13.}$$

The new e.m.f. is therefore proportional to the time rate of change of temperature multiplied by the current; the e.m.f. vanishes when there is no current. Something of this sort is, of course, demanded by symmetry considerations, for in a circuit of isotropic material with no current there is no reason why the e.m.f. should be in one direction rather than another. It is also to be noticed that the external magnetic field does not appear in the expression for the e.m.f., so that this e.m.f. is to be found in any conductor carrying a current the temperature of which is changing.

General considerations suggest that an e.m.f. of this kind is not impossible. The fact that the external magnetic field has dropped out is to be expected because of the theorem of elementary electrodynamics that there is no mutual energy between permanent magnets and currents. The effect must be connected with the self magnetic field of the current, and doubtless involves the " internal self-induction " due to the energy associated with that part of the magnetic field inside the material of the conductor itself. Some of the electrons which constitute the current have components of velocity at right angles to the self magnetic field, and these are acted on by a Hall E.M.F. which will have a component along the original current. Since the velocity of the electrons is a function of temperature, there will be a reaction when temperature changes. The detailed explanation would be very complicated, since most of the terms of the analysis would cancel from the final result, as, for example, terms due to the magnetic field of all distant parts of the current.

Under ordinary conditions this new E.M.F. would be most difficult to detect, because the temperature of a conductor cannot be changed so rapidly but that the natural decay of the current due to Joulean heating is overwhelming.

As temperature approaches 0° Abs it is highly probable that this new E.M.F. vanishes. However, because of the possibility of actually realizing persistent currents near 0° and the ease of making the experiment, it would not be superfluous to verify this by actual experiment. The suggestion just made as to the possible mechanism of the E.M.F. would demand that it vanish at 0°, because at low temperatures the electrons lose all the haphazard quality of their motion and therefore their capacity to take part in thermal effects. Also, general experience with the third law would suggest the same thing. By employing a secondary winding with mutual induction with the primary we could draw mechanical work out of the system when the current in the primary changes, that is, when there is an E.M.F. in the primary. If the new temperature E.M.F. continues to low temperatures, this means that as absolute zero is approached it would still be possible to get work out of the system merely by changing the temperature. But in all other cases of which I know this work approaches zero, and it would therefore be expected to here. If this temperature E.M.F. vanishes, this means that

$$\lim_{\tau \to 0} \frac{1}{R} \frac{\partial R}{\partial \tau} = 0. \qquad \text{VII, 14.}$$

This result is consistent with experimental results found at Leiden, although the experimental accuracy is not high.

A completely rigorous solution of this problem, not neglecting such factors as thermal expansion, may be obtained by simple methods which I have given in my "Collection of Thermodynamic Formulas."[18] Our present problem concerns a system fixed by two independent variables, τ and q_e, and is therefore entirely analogous to the simple thermodynamic systems fixed by τ and v (or p), to which the collected formulas apply. For our electromagnetic system $dW = [RIH/d]\delta q_e$, and for the simple system $dW = p\,dv$. All the formulas of the collection may be rewritten for the electromagnetic system, replacing p by RIH/d and v by q_e. In general, three independent first derivatives are needed to fix the behavior of such a system, and these must be determined by three independent measurements. Three such derivatives for the electromagnetic system would be

$$\left[\frac{\partial\left(\dfrac{RIH}{d}\right)}{\partial q_e}\right]_\tau, \left[\frac{\partial\left(\dfrac{RIH}{d}\right)}{\partial \tau}\right]_{q_e},$$

and $\left(\dfrac{\partial Q}{\partial \tau}\right)_{q_e}$. But our system does not have complete generality,

for there is a special relation, $\left(\dfrac{\partial Q}{\partial q_e}\right)_\tau = 0$, which means that there

are only two instead of three independent first derivatives to be determined by experiment. To the degree of approximation employed above, neglecting thermal expansion, one of these derivatives is $\dfrac{\partial R}{\partial \tau}$; the other corresponds to a specific heat, $\left(\dfrac{\partial Q}{\partial \tau}\right)_{q_e}$.

This specific heat must be independently determined by experiment; it will in general be a function of the current, as we can see that it must be because there are interactions between current and heat which are involved in the existence of the new temperature E.M.F. This specific heat will be considered again later.

We may next subject the Righi-Leduc phenomenon to exactly the same analysis as that just applied to the Hall phenomenon. Physically the appearance of the two systems is different, because for heat flow there is nothing exactly analogous to the energy of self-induction of the electric current in virtue of which the current continues to circulate after the external E.M.F. is cut off. However, if we use the second form of argument, in which the irreversible phenomena are allowed to assume their full values along with the reversible phenomena, and the total changes of entropy due to all processes are put into the equations, the analysis for the thermal problem assumes the same formal appearance as that for the electrical problem.

A plate carrying a longitudinal heat current in a magnetic field experiences a transverse temperature difference, which may be utilized as source and sink of a thermodynamic engine. The transverse temperature difference in such a plate is $\Delta\tau = S'WH/d$. If the quantity of heat δq_w flows transversely between these temperature limits, it delivers to the engine an amount of work:

$$\delta W = \frac{\Delta\tau}{\tau}\,\delta q_w = \frac{S'WH}{\tau d}\,\delta q_w.$$

Exactly the same analysis as before may now be repeated, replacing δq_e by δq_w, and RIH/d by $S'WH/\tau d$. The condition that $\delta Q/\tau$ is a perfect differential is:

$$\left(\frac{\partial Q}{\partial q_w}\right)_\tau = \tau\left[\frac{\partial\left(\dfrac{S'WH}{\tau d}\right)}{\partial\tau}\right]_{q_w}.$$

Neglecting thermal expansion, and using the fact that H is fixed from outside and so not variable, this becomes

$$\left(\frac{\partial Q}{\partial q_w}\right)_\tau = \tau\frac{H}{d}\left[\frac{\partial\left(\dfrac{S'W}{\tau}\right)}{\partial\tau}\right]_{q_w}, \qquad \text{VII, 15.}$$

or, written for specific quantities:

$$\left(\frac{\partial Q'}{\partial q'_w}\right)_\tau = \tau H\left[\frac{\partial\left(\dfrac{S'w}{\tau}\right)}{\partial\tau}\right]_{q'_w}. \qquad \text{VII, 16.}$$

Exactly the same two arguments from symmetry apply as before, from which it follows that this heating effect must vanish, or $\left(\dfrac{\partial Q'}{\partial q'_w}\right)_\tau = 0$. Whence,

$$\frac{1}{\Sigma}\left(\frac{\partial\Sigma}{\partial\tau}\right)_{q_w} = -\frac{1}{W}\left(\frac{\partial W}{\partial\tau}\right)_{q_w} = -\frac{1}{w}\left(\frac{\partial w}{\partial\tau}\right)_{q_w}, \qquad \text{VII, 17.}$$

introducing the new quantity $\Sigma \equiv S'/\tau$, and using the density, w, of heat flow instead of the total quantity of heat.

$\dfrac{1}{\Sigma}\dfrac{\partial\Sigma}{\partial\tau}$ is an independent parameter, which must be determined by experiment, and over which thermodynamics has no control.

The measurement of Σ itself is a matter of great experimental difficulty, to say nothing of $\dfrac{\partial\Sigma}{\partial\tau}$, so that from the experimental point of view we are rather in the dark here. If $\dfrac{\partial\Sigma}{\partial\tau} \neq 0$, and it would be a coincidence if it were exactly zero, then $\left(\dfrac{\partial w}{\partial\tau}\right)_{q_w} \neq 0$, and we have here the formal analogy of the new temperature E.M.F., just discussed, that is, a thermo-motive force in a conductor carrying a thermal current depending on the rate of change of temperature. Of course, from symmetry considerations, this thermo-motive force must be proportional to the heat current, as before. If there is such an effect, the mechanism must be very different from that in the corresponding electrical case, because of the absence of a thermal self-induction. However, there must be an energy associated with a thermal current in virtue of which the total energy content of a body carrying a thermal current is different from that of the same body without a thermal current, because there is something analogous to velocity associated with a thermal current (connected with the velocity of propagation of elastic disturbances), and hence of necessity something analogous to space density of energy. It is this energy source which must be involved in the thermo-motive force and which gives a value to $\dfrac{\partial w}{\partial\tau}$ different from zero.

The Ettingshausen and the Nernst effects may next be subject to an exactly similar analysis. Work can be extracted from a system in which there is an Ettingshausen temperature difference by allowing a transverse thermal current to flow, and similarly work may be extracted from a system exhibiting a Nernst potential difference by allowing a transverse electrical current to flow. The results of the analysis, written for specific quantities, are :

$$\left(\frac{\partial Q'}{\partial q'_w}\right)_\tau = \tau H \frac{\partial}{\partial\tau}\left(\frac{iP}{\tau}\right)_{q'_w} \qquad \text{VII, 18.}$$

and
$$\left(\frac{\partial Q'}{\partial q'_e}\right)_\tau = \tau H \frac{\partial}{\partial\tau}\,(wQ')_{q'_e}. \qquad \text{VII, 19.}$$

The Q' on the right-hand side of equation 19 (the modified Nernst coefficient) will not be confused with the Q' on the left (the heat per unit volume).

The same situation as before now does not hold with respect to the vanishing of these two thermal effects. The first argument fails at once because thermal and electric currents do not combine vectorially, and the second argument, from symmetry, does not carry through either. There is, however, a connection between the two heats because of the connection between P and Q'.

Abbreviate $\dfrac{P}{\tau}$ by Π, and write the two equations for heat absorbed per unit time in terms of densities of electrical and thermal currents. Equation 18 becomes

$$\frac{\partial Q'}{\partial t} = \tau H w_t i_l \Pi \left(\frac{1}{i}\frac{\partial i}{\partial \tau} + \frac{1}{\Pi}\frac{\partial \Pi}{\partial \tau}\right), \qquad \text{VII, 20.}$$

and equation 19 becomes

$$\frac{\partial Q'}{\partial t} = \tau H i_t w_l Q' \left(\frac{1}{w}\frac{\partial w}{\partial \tau} + \frac{1}{Q'}\frac{\partial Q'}{\partial \tau}\right). \qquad \text{VII, 21.}$$

The factors in square brackets are constants of the material, true scalars, independent of sign convention, as may be seen by inspection. Since the designation transverse or longitudinal is of no significance, the heat on the left-hand sides must be the same when unit electric and thermal currents flow in any actual system. The subscripts may be dropped from the w's and i's therefore, but a proper sign convention must be retained. In equation 20 the convention is that wi is positive if anti-clockwise rotation through 90° carries the direction of w into that of i, and in equation 21 the convention is the opposite. But now the physical situation should be describable with either convention; if the convention of equation 21 is applied to equation 20, the sign of wi reverses, but Π is also subject to a sign convention, and the convention of equation 21 reverses the sign of Π. Hence everything is consistent, and the conclusion cannot be drawn that the heating effects must vanish, a conclusion which I erroneously, according to my present opinion, drew in my original *Physical Review* paper. But another conclusion may be drawn, because we have already shown that $\Pi = Q'$. Hence the physical constants in square brackets in the two equations must be equal, or :

$$\frac{1}{i}\frac{\partial i}{\partial \tau} + \frac{1}{\Pi}\frac{\partial \Pi}{\partial \tau} = \frac{1}{w}\frac{\partial w}{\partial \tau} + \frac{1}{Q'}\frac{\partial Q'}{\partial \tau}. \qquad \text{VII, 22.}$$

The derivatives in Π and Q' cancel. But $\dfrac{\partial i}{\partial \tau}$ is the same $\dfrac{\partial i}{\partial \tau}$ that has already occurred in analysis of the Hall effect, for the significance of the partial derivative in both cases is that no work is done by the system during change of temperature. In the same way, the $\dfrac{\partial w}{\partial \tau}$ is the same as the $\dfrac{\partial w}{\partial \tau}$ of the analysis of the Righi-Leduc effect. Hence we may substitute the values found for these in 12 and 17 and obtain :

$$\frac{1}{R}\frac{\partial R}{\partial \tau} = \frac{1}{\Sigma}\frac{\partial \Sigma}{\partial \tau}, \qquad \text{VII, 23.}$$

or $\qquad \Sigma = \text{Const } R, \quad \text{or} \quad S' = \text{Const } \tau R. \qquad \text{VII, 24.}$

Σ, therefore, goes to zero at $0°$ Abs in the same way as R. It is to be noticed that this relation at once settles the question as to the existence of a temperature thermo-motive force, about which the previous discussion left us in some doubt because of experimental uncertainty as to whether $\dfrac{1}{\Sigma}\dfrac{\partial \Sigma}{\partial \tau}$ was really different from zero or not.

In my *Physical Review* paper, by equating $\dfrac{\partial Q'}{\partial t}$ to zero in equations 20 and 21, an additional relation was deduced which demanded that P/τ and Q' also be constants multiplied by R. This relation must now be given up, so that thus far we have only two relations between the four transverse coefficients,

$$S' = \text{Const } \tau R, \quad \text{and} \quad P = \tau Q'.$$

This is as far as I have been able to get in the purely thermodynamic deduction of relations. There is, however, another possible relation which it is tempting to record here. We have already seen from our thermo-electric analysis that an electric current convects with it the thermal energy $\tau \int_0^\tau \dfrac{\sigma\, d\tau}{\tau}$. Phenomena due to this thermal current should therefore be superposed on those due to the electrical current in the Hall phenomenon. We have such a phenomenon immediately at hand in the Ettingshausen phenomenon. It seems plausible to postulate that the Ettingshausen temperature difference is merely the Righi-Leduc temperature difference associated with the thermal energy convected by the electrical current. We have :

Ettingshausen temperature gradient $= PiH$
Righi-Leduc temperature gradient $\ \ = S'wH$

Equating these two gradients, and putting $w = i\tau \int_0^\tau \dfrac{\sigma\, d\tau}{\tau}$ gives at once :

$$P = \tau S' \int_0^\tau \frac{\sigma\, d\tau}{\tau}. \hspace{2cm} \text{VII, 25.}$$

This suspected relation cannot be tested accurately by experiment, because, for one thing, σ is not known as a function of temperature for most metals. A very rough test can be made by replacing $\int_0^\tau \dfrac{\sigma\, d\tau}{\tau}$ by σ, which has the same dimensions. With this substitution, a not bad check with experiment is obtained, so that the relation is not impossible, and we would seem to be justified in concluding that at least an important part of the Ettingshausen temperature difference must be due to the Righi-Leduc action on the thermal energy convected by the electric current. Detailed pictures of the conduction mechanism would suggest, however, that the relation cannot be exact. One would expect the Righi-Leduc effect to be concerned only with that part of the thermal conduction in metals which is done by the electron mechanism, for the atomic thermal conduction should not be affected by a magnetic field. Since, however, it is probable that the electron part of thermal conduction is by far the larger part, as suggested by the approximate constancy of the Wiedemann

Franz ratio, we may suspect that the relation between P and S' just deduced will not be far from correct, with P somewhat smaller than $\tau S' \displaystyle\int_0^\tau \frac{\sigma\, d\tau}{\tau}$.

Finally, we discuss certain small effects which we have hitherto neglected, but the existence of which may nevertheless be deduced from the analysis above. There is in the first place a heating effect associated with a change of current; this may be deduced from the fact that current changes when temperature changes. Consider a circuit in which current is flowing, neglecting Joulean decay. This circuit is made to deliver energy by inserting in it an E.M.F. which receives work from the current in virtue of the energy stored as electrodynamic energy of self-induction and any coupling of the thermal energy with the energy of self-induction. Call ϵ the arbitrary E.M.F. Take as the variables fixing the condition of the system τ and i. The E.M.F. ϵ must balance the total E.M.F. in the circuit; one term comes from the change of i with time through the self induction, and the second term is the temperature E.M.F. already considered, which arises when temperature is changing. The E.M.F. equation is therefore :

$$\epsilon = L \frac{di}{dt} + iL \frac{1}{R} \frac{\partial R}{\partial \tau} \frac{d\tau}{dt}. \qquad \text{VII, 26.}$$

The first law, written for unit time, gives,

$$\frac{dQ}{dt} = \frac{dW}{dt} + \frac{dE}{dt},$$

where E is internal energy. But $\dfrac{dW}{dt} = \epsilon i$. Whence, substituting the value for ϵ, and setting $\dfrac{dE}{dt} = \dfrac{\partial E}{\partial \tau} \dfrac{d\tau}{dt} + \dfrac{\partial E}{\partial i} \dfrac{di}{dt}$,

$$\frac{dQ}{dt} = \left(\frac{\partial E}{\partial \tau} + i^2 L \frac{1}{R} \frac{\partial R}{\partial \tau} \right) \frac{d\tau}{dt} + \left(\frac{\partial E}{\partial i} + iL \right) \frac{di}{dt}.$$

Divide by τ, obtaining $\dfrac{dS}{dt}$. Divide out the dt, and write the condition that dS be a perfect differential by equating the cross derivatives of the coefficients, and obtain :

$$\left(\frac{\partial Q}{\partial i}\right)_\tau = - \ 2 \ \tau i L \ \frac{1}{R} \frac{\partial R}{\partial \tau}, \qquad \text{VII, 27.}$$

neglecting the thermal expansion of the circuit, that is, setting

$$\frac{\partial L}{\partial \tau} = 0.$$

That is, an inflow of heat is required to maintain temperature constant when current is altered.   If thermal expansion is not negligible, there is an additional heating equal to $\tau i \dfrac{dL}{d\tau}$.   In terms of the ordinary specific heat this expression may be made at once to give an approximate value for the adiabatic change of temperature when current is altered adiabatically.   The right-hand side of equation 27 contains only measurable quantities.   I have calculated that in a toroid of bismuth, of 10 cm radius and 1 cm thickness, the change of temperature when current is increased from 0 to 100 amp/cm^2 is of the order of $10^{-13°}$ C.   The effect is doubtless much too small to be directly detected under any attainable conditions.

This temperature change is evidently connected with the thermal energy convected by the current.   The amount of the convected energy is known; if its velocity of flow were also known, its space density would be known, and we could calculate the thermal energy set free when current changes.   The same considerations demand that the specific heat of a conductor carrying a current be different from that of the same conductor without a current, for the thermal energy convected by the current is a function of temperature, and an additional term is therefore needed to increase this energy when temperature changes.   We may make a rough calculation of the order of magnitudes for cobalt, which has an unusually large σ and therefore an unusually large convected energy.   As before, replace $\tau \displaystyle\int_0^\tau \frac{\sigma \, d\tau}{\tau}$ by $\tau\sigma$ as a sufficiently good approximation. σ for cobalt is 2.2×10^{-6}

volts/° C. Therefore at 0° C one coulomb convects with it $(273 \times 2.2 \times 10^{-6})/4.2 = 1.4 \times 10^{-4}$ gm cal, which is the thermal energy convected across 1 cm^2 in 1 sec by 1 amp. About the velocity with which this is convected we are entirely in the dark, so we can only make experiments to find something plausible. We assume in the first place that the velocity is the same as the mean velocity of all the electrons taking part in the conduction. If we assume, as in Sommerfeld's theory, one free electron per atom, the mean velocity of drift of the electrons in a current of 1 amp/cm^2 turns out to be 6×10^{-5} cm/sec for cobalt. This demands a density of energy of 2.3 gm cal/cm^3. Since this energy is proportional to τ, this would demand an increase in the specific heat of about 1% in a conductor carrying 1 amp/cm^2. Such an effect is doubtless much too large to be admissible. Probably the direct measurement of specific heat with current flowing has not been attempted, but the apparent self-induction of such a material would be a function of temperature as well as of the geometrical dimensions, since electromagnetic energy could come out of temperature changes, and since the formulas for self-induction as a function of dimensions only have been most carefully checked, we may assume that any such contribution to the specific heat is absolutely ruled out. A more natural assumption would seem to be that the current convects heat, not with the mean velocity of *drift* of the electrons, but with the mean velocity of the electrons themselves. The mean velocity of the electrons in a Fermi-Dirac gas, such as is demanded by present electrical theory, is of the order of that imparted by 5 volts, or approximately 1.3×10^8 cm/sec. This would give a space density only 5×10^{-13} of that above, so that all the corresponding effects would be very far below the reach of experiment. Another plausible assumption would be that the convected energy is closely connected with the velocity of sound, since it is well established that thermal conduction is nothing more than the disorganized conduction of mechanical energy by elastic waves of molecular lengths. The velocity of sound in cobalt is 5×10^5 cm/sec, and this again would give such a low space density for the thermal energy convected by the electric current that any effects would be most difficult to establish by direct experiment.

Analogous considerations may be applied to thermal currents. We have already seen that there must be a thermo-motive force in a body carrying a thermal current when the temperature changes because of the relation $\frac{1}{w}\frac{\partial w}{\partial \tau} = -\frac{1}{\Sigma}\frac{\partial \Sigma}{\partial \tau}$. Just as in the electrical case, we might go on and deduce a more exact expression for the thermo-motive force which is involved in the term $\frac{\partial w}{\partial \tau}$ if we had more definite information as to the store of energy which is tapped by the action of the thermo-motive force. In the electrical case it was plausible enough to assume that this energy was mostly the energy of self-induction. In the thermal case, however, there is no thermal self-induction, and the only store of energy which presents itself is the space density of energy associated with the thermal stream. One can experiment with various possibilities here by making various assumptions about the velocity of the stream. Perhaps the most natural assumption is that the velocity is the same as the velocity of sound, as would be suggested by the Debye picture of thermal conduction. In copper this velocity is 3.5×10^5 cm/sec. Imagine a cube of copper one cm on a side, with two opposite faces maintained at a difference of temperature of 100°. The thermal flux is approximately 100 cal/sec. If this is moving with the velocity of sound, a space density of $100/3.5 \times 10^5 = 3 \times 10^{-4}$ gm cal/cm³ is involved, and the energy content of the copper cube is greater by this amount in virtue of the thermal current flowing through it. The normal heat capacity of the cube is about 0.8 gm cal. Hence if the copper cube could be suddenly isolated from source and sink of heat supply, the final temperature, after heat flow had ceased and equilibrium had been reached, would be 4×10^{-4}° C higher than the average temperature during flow. This would doubtless be impossible to detect experimentally. However, if the proper velocity to associate with the heat flow were not the velocity of sound, but something of the order of a few cm/sec, which is the order of the apparent velocity with which maxima and minima of periodic disturbances sink into the metal (there is no true velocity in this case), then a temperature change on stopping heat flow of many degrees would be found, which is certainly not permitted by experiment. This is in so far confirmatory evidence of the correctness of the Debye picture of thermal conduction.

In general, because of the existence of the term $\dfrac{1}{w}\dfrac{\partial w}{\partial \tau}$, there will be heating effects when the thermal currents are altered, just as in the electrical case, but the effects are so small that I shall not pursue the matter further except to remark that the effects are proportional to absolute temperature. The method of attack in order to calculate these exceedingly small effects has already been sufficiently indicated.

CHAPTER VIII

CONNECTIONS WITH ELECTRON THEORY OF METALS AND PHOTO-ELECTRIC PHENOMENA

A complete electron theory of metals must ultimately describe in detail not only the mechanism actually responsible for all the necessary relations which we have deduced by thermodynamics, but must go further and deduce correct values for all those parameters about which thermodynamics can have nothing to say. This latter part of the problem is doubtless by far the most interesting, but consideration of it is beyond the scope of this book. The first part of the problem, however, is also of interest, and we shall now have to examine the picture which electron theory gives of some of the phenomena which we have been discussing. Modern electron theory so modifies the fundamental picture of photoelectric phenomena that the thermodynamic discussion appropriate to the older picture has to be changed, and so has had to be postponed until after a presentation of the present electron point of view.

Let us begin with a very brief and elementary presentation of the fundamentals of the present wave mechanical theory of metals. The most important new idea brought to this field by wave mechanics is due to Sommerfeld, who applied the Pauli exclusion principle to the free electrons in a metal and showed that they must be in the condition of a degenerate gas at ordinary temperatures, although a gas composed of ordinary atoms exhibits this degree of degeneration only in the neighborhood of 0° Abs. The result is that in a metal at ordinary temperatures the free electrons fill solidly full the lower floors of the " energy skyscraper," to employ the vivid picture of Frenkel,[19] and only in the very few upper occupied floors is there any freedom of migration back and forth between the various apartments. This restlessness in the few upper floors is temperature agitation; the great bulk of the electrons are unaffected by temperature, although nevertheless possessing kinetic energy of motion very much greater on the average than the temperature energy that was demanded by the classical theory. At 0° Abs all the electrons settle down and pack solidly the lower floors of the energy sky-scraper until their numbers are exhausted. This means that there is a definite upper limit to the kinetic energy of the electrons at 0° Abs, which may be called W_0. As temperature rises, the upper limit loses its sharpness, and electrons may spasmodically appear in the still higher energy levels, the frequency of appearance increasing with temperature. Figure 28, taken from a paper by Nordheim,[20] shows the number

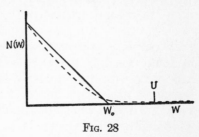

FIG. 28

of electrons with given component of kinetic energy *normal to the surface* of the metal as a function of the kinetic energy normal to the surface, the normal component being the only component important for our immediate purposes. The heavy line represents the distribution at 0° Abs, the dotted line the distribution at some higher temperature. The area under the dotted line is the same as that under the full line, and represents the total number of electrons.

The increase of total energy of the electrons with rising temperature may be computed; it is much less than demanded by the classical gas laws, as can be at once seen qualitatively. At room temperature the specific heat of the electrons turns out to be only one sixtieth of the classical value. Thus at one stroke is solved the difficulty of the classical theory with the specific heats.

The electrons would diffuse right out of the metal, in virtue of their velocity if it were not for some sort of restraining action. Of course when an electron leaves the metal, a positive charge is left behind which tends to prevent the escape of further electrons. The process of electron escape would thus in any event be ultimately prevented by the building up of a surface charge, but this does not seem to be the agency actually at work. For if this were the case, we should find experimentally that metals surround themselves with a constant field of force and a constant density of surface charge, independent of their shape, and this is not the case, but rather metals come to characteristic differences of *potential*, the electric forces involved being large or small, depending on the geometrical configuration. We have already met a re-straining surface action in the double layer that we have seen is involved in the existence of the Volta potential difference, and such an effect may be involved here. Modern theory postulates, therefore, the existence at the boundary of every metal of a characteristic barrier of some sort, such that a definite amount of work, characteristic of the metal, must be done by the electron in passing from the interior of the metal to free external space. If the interior electron possesses an amount of kinetic energy normal to the surface greater than this characteristic amount, which is usually called U and is not to be confused with the U of earlier chapters, the electron escapes; otherwise it remains inside the metal.

This picture at once provides the possibility of thermionic emission. The characteristic energy U is indicated in the Figure 28. At any temperature greater than $0°$ Abs the diagram shows that some of the electrons have a greater normal kinetic energy than U, and hence will escape, constituting the thermionic current. The number having the requisite energy evidently increases as temperature increases. One can see qualitatively from the figure that the difference between the energy U and the maximum energy at $0°$ Abs, W_0, will be a decisive factor in determining the number that escape. This difference, $U - W_0$, is called the " work function."

The situation is complicated by the possibility of reflection of some of the fast electrons at the surface. To work this out in detail involves assumptions about the distribution of force in the barrier zone, and does not affect the fundamental argument.   The final result is that this picture yields for the spontaneously emitted current the expression :

$$i = \frac{4 \pi m e \kappa^2}{h^3} \overline{D} \tau^2 \epsilon^{-\frac{U - W_0}{\kappa \tau}} , \qquad \text{VIII, 1.}$$

where $\overline{D}$ is the so-called diffusion coefficient, which is at most equal to unity, and is presumably not greatly less. A formula is thus found of the exact form of that previously obtained for the thermionic emission, IV, 33, in which the spin factor G has been set equal to 2, and which is known to check with experiment.

Next consider the situation when two different metals are in contact with each other at constant temperature. The system comes to equilibrium with a characteristic Volta difference of potential between the external surfaces. Consider first what happens at $0°$ Abs. The maximum kinetic energy of the internal electrons, W_0, is a function of the metal and may in fact be calculated. Suppose that W_{0B} is greater than W_{0A}; this means

that the maximum kinetic energy normal to the surface of the electrons in B is greater than that in A, so that an uncompensated stream of electrons would pass from B to A unless there were some restraining action at the boundary. This restraining action must be of the nature of a

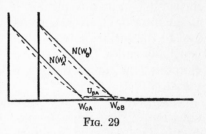

Fig. 29

potential barrier like that on the external surface, such that the loss of kinetic energy of an electron on passing through the barrier is exactly equal to the characteristic difference $W_{0B} - W_{0A}$. Call this difference U_{BA}. With this restraining action there is equilibrium between the electrons in B and A. Electrons pass from A to B, being speeded up in the interfacial region, their maximum kinetic energy being increased from W_{0A} to W_{0B} and their minimum from 0 to U_{BA}, whereas an equal stream of electrons passes from B to A, those starting with the maximum kinetic energy W_{0B} reaching A with the energy W_{0A}, those with kinetic energy U_{BA} just penetrating the interface and arriving in A with 0 velocity, whereas none with energy less than U_{BA} are able to penetrate at all. Equilibrium demands that the number of electrons leaving with any kinetic energy be equal to the number entering with the same energy. This shows at once that the distribution function for the electrons in A and B must be of exactly the same form, one curve being displaced with respect to the other by the amount U_{BA}, as indicated in Figure 29.

Consider next what is demanded by equilibrium in the space outside the metals in which there is the Volta difference of potential. Start with an electron at rest in A; carry it through the surface, doing on it the work U_A; carry it across to the external surface of B, doing in addition the work eV_{AB}; carry it to the interior of B, receiving the work U_B; and carry it through the interface back to A, doing the work U_{BA}. The total amount of work done must be zero, because this is an isothermal operation, and therefore,

$$U_A + eV_{AB} + U_{BA} = U_B,$$

or $$V_{AB} = \frac{1}{e}[U_B - U_A - U_{BA}], \qquad \text{VIII, 2.}$$

and we have an expression for the Volta difference in terms of the characteristic barrier actions. The relations are indicated in

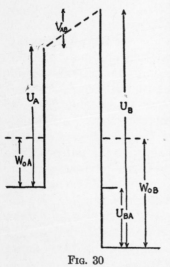

Figure 30, taken from Frenkel except for a change of sign of V_{AB}. Exactly the same sort of a cycle may be described starting with an electron of any kinetic energy level in A; at every stage of the process the electron has this constant kinetic energy in excess of the energy of the electron which started from rest, and it returns to its starting point with its initial kinetic energy. The same condition that expresses equilibrium for electrons of one initial kinetic energy therefore expresses it for all.

Exactly the same considerations apply to equilibrium at any temperature, from which it is again to be concluded that the curve of energy distribution for any metal at any temperature is the same as that for any other metal at the same temperature, except for a displacement along the energy axis of amount U_{BA}. This con-

Fig. 30

clusion, reached by arguments strictly thermodynamic in spirit, is supported by the detailed expressions for the distribution which have been worked out by wave mechanics.

It is evident, therefore, that there is a close parallelism between certain features of the detailed electron theory picture and the picture to which we have been led on general grounds. We now wish to go further and find the exact correspondence. In particular, what corresponds in the general picture to the barrier, U, which keeps the electrons in the metal? An inspection of the wave mechanics analysis shows at once that there is included in U *all* the forces which act on the electron as it struggles out through the surface, including not only the electrostatic forces arising from any electrostatic double layer, but also any forces which the individual electron may call into play by the displacement of other electrons as it passes through the surface. The " image force " is of this latter character; it is what we have called a " non-electrostatic force." Furthermore, consideration of numerical magnitudes shows that the work done by the image force is of the same order of magnitude as the Volta potential jump, and may therefore be expected to be at least an important part of the whole effect. The ordinary quantum analysis makes no attempt to split the total effect, U, into contributions made by image force and double layer separately. However, the mere existence of a Volta jump demands double layers somewhere, so that the situation cannot be met by supposing that U arises only from the image force. The analysis of U into different parts is most important when one attempts to describe the nature of the energy transformations. In our original thermionic emission formula the η_0 was a latent *heat*, which in principle could be measured by experiment. If the wave mechanics formula is essentially the same, then the exponential term $U - W_0$ must also be a *heat*. Now there can be no thermal effects associated with that part of U which arises from an electrostatic double layer, because, as we have already seen, the energy involved in the passage of electricity through a double layer is a purely electrodynamic affair, the mechanism of transfer being the Poynting vector. If, then, $U - W_0$ is a heat, the electrostatic double layer contribution to U must be small. We must further assume that the work done by the image force eventually manifests itself as a heat. This is a not intrinsically improbable assumption, because the work done on the electron by the image force is provided at the expense of disarrangements in the positions of the other electrons in the metal, and these disarranged electrons may draw on the general store of thermal energy of the body in working back to their undisturbed positions. It is not at all evident, however, that *all* the work done by the image force is thermal in character; if a single electron leaves the metal, the metal is left with a charge, and some of the work of the image force might come from the miscellaneous supply of non-thermal potential energy of the metal. Or, if the departure of the electron is compensated by the entrance of another electron at the other side of the metal, there may be a non-thermal flow of electrodynamic energy on the Poynting vector from the region of one image force to the region of the other. There is another difficulty at low temperature. As $0°$ Abs is approached, the energy $U - W_0$ must still remain thermal; it is not pleasant to think that the work of the image force, which is concerned merely with rearrangements in the condensed phase, should remain thermal at $0°$ Abs. In the gaseous phase, on the other hand, the density decreases so rapidly at low temperatures that the gas remains outside the region of quantum phenomena, and thermal effects may persist.

The logical conclusion of the argument that electrostatic jumps can involve no thermal effects would seem to be that the entire Volta jump occur at the metal — metal interface, which was Kelvin's original point of view as opposed to that of Maxwell and Heaviside. If one further assumes that it is only electrostatic forces which are accompanied by non-thermal effects, one would have at $0°$ Abs, since there are no thermal effects (that is, Peltier heat) at $0°$, $eV_{AB} = -U_{BA}$ in equation 2, which would involve $U_A = U_B$ for all metals. But U_A is capable of measurement in terms of electron diffraction effects in the crystal and the change of electron wave length when the electron enters the metal from the outside. Experiments have been made to date on only a few metals and the accuracy is not high, so that it cannot be stated whether this conclusion agrees with experiment or not. On the other hand, Frenkel [21] has a theory of the structure of the double layer in terms of the structure of the atoms (protons inside and electrons outside) which would demand double layers at the inter- face metal-vacuum. The situation is therefore not as clean-cut as one would like to think.

At any rate, it seems unsatisfactory to me to assume offhand, as wave mechanics apparently does, that the work done by the image forces is compensated by *heat* inflow. There is another consideration that demands that the mechanism that is respon- sible for the image force, or in general the mechanism that is responsible for the U, should receive much more careful discus- sion than it has apparently yet received. If the exponent $U - W_0$ of the thermionic emission formula contains an appreciable term proportional to τ, the formula may be rewritten with a different constant factor in front of the exponential. Now the experi- ments demand that the factor have about the value given. It would seem, therefore, that wave mechanics should hardly be satisfied with its reproduction of the emission formula until it has shown that $U - W_0$ is nearly independent of temperature.

In general, from the very nature of its attack, I do not see how wave mechanics can give a complete solution of the problem, but it can only show that its demands are not inconsistent with the actual situation, as it has done here. For the quantities which enter the fundamental equations of wave mechanics are merely the energy changes in which the electron is concerned, and no attempt is made to analyze this energy into two aspects, thermal and mechanical. But thermodynamics, on the other hand, rec- ognizes thermal and mechanical aspects of energy, and further- more these two aspects are physically real, because experiment can distinguish between energy absorbed as heat and energy absorbed as mechanical (or electrodynamic) work. Until wave mechanics devises some method for analyzing energy into its two aspects, it seems to me that the problem is only half solved, although there is no denying the importance of the half that has been solved.

One may go further and question whether the general method of attack adopted by quantum theory hitherto is broad enough to meet the general situation in a metal. If electricity in the metal may be like a gas and receive work as a product of a pressure and a change of volume, as it certainly does in the external electron gas, then the work done on the electron cannot always be represented as the product of something into the *displacement* of the electron, and this is the only kind of work considered by the usual wave mechanics analysis.

Until it is possible to decide what part of the energy U_{BA} comes from a double layer and what part from other sources, it would seem to be futile to attempt to find what corresponds in the present electron picture to the Peltier heat at an interface.

Although the wave mechanics picture thus does not appear to be particularly successful in clearing up the questions of detail presented by thermionic emission, it is quite otherwise with respect to photo-electric emission. Here it has modified the older concepts, and furthermore the modification is being found to agree with experiment. Consider first the situation at 0° Abs. If an electron is to escape from the metal, it must abstract from the radiation enough energy to enable it to leap the potential barrier. The electrons of maximum energy, W_0, will require the least additional energy, which is $U - W_0$. If this energy is abstracted from radiation of frequency ν_0, we have by the quantum relation $h\nu_0 = U - W_0$ for the minimum frequency of incident radiation that can cause the emission of any electrons; all such electrons emerge with zero velocity. This is exactly according to Einstein's original picture. What now happens if light of frequency ν, greater than ν_0, falls on the metal? Einstein's point of view declared that since the energy $h\nu$ is now abstracted from the radiation, and an energy $h\nu_0$ is necessary to get out of the metal, all of the electrons will emerge with an energy $h(\nu - \nu_0)$, that is, all the emergent electrons will have a single definite velocity. This picture therefore evidently represented all the electrons in the metal as originally at rest. But the new picture demands that electrons with a range of velocities be emitted, because all those electrons will now obviously be able to struggle through the barrier if their original kinetic energy, W, added to that which they receive from the radiation, $h\nu$, is equal to or greater than U. Hence electrons with a range of energies will be emitted, their original energies in the metal being between W_0 and $W = U - h\nu$, and their emergent energies being between $W_0 + h\nu - U$ and 0.

Experimentally, the distribution of the emergent electrons through an energy range is known to exist; the older theory explained this by secondary dissipation effects, perhaps due to collisions between the atoms and those electrons originating in the depths of the metal. The new picture represents the distribution as a primary effect, not involving any dissipation, and therefore presumably reversible.

At temperatures above 0° Abs the picture is qualitatively quite altered. There are now within the metal a few electrons of any velocity, and hence there is always some emission, even without the stimulus of radiation. The effect of radiation of low frequencies is merely to increase somewhat the normal thermionic emission. But this we have seen to be imperceptibly small at ordinary temperatures, and the photo-electric emission at low frequencies is also imperceptibly small. As the critical frequency ν_0 is approached, photo-electric emission increases somewhat, as may be seen qualitatively from Figure 31, and then beyond ν_0 the increase of emission is very rapid, because now approximately the same store of electrons is available that was available at 0° Abs. At normal temperatures, therefore, there is not a sharp photo-electric threshold, but merely a range in which the emission increases rapidly, and this range becomes wider and more blurred the higher the temperature.

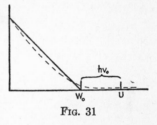

Fig. 31

This picture entirely alters the attitude of the experimenter. It was formerly believed that the photo-electric threshold should be sharp, and failure to find a sharp threshold was attributed to faulty experimental conditions, such as surface films due to imperfect vacuum. This mistaken view has, as a matter of historical fact, had no bad effect, because it is true that photo-electric phenomena are exceedingly sensitive to surface conditions, and by improving the vacuum technique more reproducible results have been obtained, and the photo-electric limit has become continually sharper until within the last few years. It now appears that vacuum technique has been so improved that sufficiently clean surfaces can be obtained to justify the expectation that the effect of still remaining surface contaminations is negligible, and that the lack of definiteness which now remains in the photo-electric threshold and its apparent change with temperature is the actual effect which the wave mechanics picture would lead us to expect. Since the effect of temperature on the departure of the electron distribution from that at $0°$ Abs may be calculated theoretically, it should be possible from a sufficiently accurate photo-electric emission curve at any temperature to calculate back to ν_0, the threshold frequency at $0°$ Abs. Fowler [22] has in fact shown how to make this calculation, using the most recent experimental data obtained at the University of Wisconsin by Mendenhall and his co-workers, and obtains a satisfactory check. Since agreement within experimental error is obtained in this way, the conclusion is justified that $U - W_0$, which is equal to ν_0 at $0°$ Abs, cannot vary greatly with temperature. The experimental accuracy is still, however, probably not sufficiently high to justify this statement to any considerable degree of precision, and there are in fact for one or two metals temperature anomalies which have not been explained.

If $U - W_0$ is independent of temperature, the wave mechanics picture evidently demands that the photo-electric threshhold be the same as the thermionic work function in formula 1. This equality is certainly approximately satisfied as a matter of experiment, but until experimental accuracy is higher and we have more definite ideas as to possible variations of U with temperature, it would seem that the equality cannot be established with any considerable accuracy. This is the sort of question that one would expect to be answerable by thermodynamic methods of attack. In several papers [23] I examined this question, and proved thermodynamically certain connections between the phenomena of photo-electric emission and thermionic emission, and in particular the equality of $h\nu_0$ and the η_0 of the thermionic emission formula. The equivalence of $h\nu_0$ and $U - W_0$ cannot be established by thermodynamics because $U - W_0$ does not have complete thermodynamic status until the question of its variation with temperature is settled. My discussion, however, assumed the older point of view about photo-electric phenomena; it was assumed that at every temperature there is a sharp threshold, that this threshold might be a function of the temperature, and that under the stimulus of light of a single frequency electrons of only a single velocity are emitted. Since this picture must now be given up, and in particular since " temperature coefficient of photo-electric threshold " no longer has any definite meaning, the treatment must evidently be modified. However, since the former picture was approximately correct, it must be that its conclusions are approximately correct. Otherwise we should be led to the impossible conclusion that none of the results of present thermodynamic analysis can apply in practice, because certainly all of our experimental assumptions are subject to some degree of error.

The simplest result of my former analysis can be retained without much modification; this was a thermodynamic proof of the necessity of the experimental fact, particularly insisted upon by Millikan,[24] that the " stopping potentials " of all pure metals under photo-electric stimulation are the same. The experimental meaning of this is as follows. Given a metal A exposed to the action of light of frequency ν under the stimulation of which it emits photo-electrons toward some other metal B. A potential is applied with a battery between A and B of such a magnitude as just to prevent any of the emitted electrons from reaching B. This potential is called the " stopping potential," and the experimental fact is that it is independent of the metal A, depending only on ν and the metal B. Millikan showed that an equivalent way of expressing the same relation, assuming the Einstein photo-electric equation, is :

$$V_{AB} = \left(\frac{h}{e}\right)(\nu_{0B} - \nu_{0A}). \qquad \text{VIII, 3.}$$

It is now evident that this experimental fact is only an approximate expression of the actual state of affairs, because some electrons of any velocity are emitted by any metal at any temperature above 0° Abs, and therefore there is, strictly speaking, no sharp stopping potential, but only a potential at which a very rapid change begins. We shall, therefore, in the theoretical discussion assume in the first place that the metal is at 0° Abs.

Construct a parallel plate condenser of two metals A and B, which confront each other in vacuum at 0° Abs. The two metals may now be assumed to have sharp photo-electric thresholds ν_{0A} and ν_{0B}, and furthermore to come to a definite Volta difference of potential V_{AB}. Let us suppose that ν_{0B} is greater than ν_{0A}, and let us fill the space between A and B uniformly with radiation of frequency ν_{0B}, traveling in straight lines back and forth between A and B, without deviation, except as it may be absorbed to produce a photo-electric electron. The nature of this radiation, and how it shall be treated thermodynamically, has to be carefully considered. Light of a single definite frequency can in no sense be described as thermal radiation. Thermal radiation spreads out over a range of frequencies, with a thermodynamically determined distribution of intensity, and there is a continual interchange of energy back and forth among the frequencies, as is demanded by statistical equilibrium. It is impossible to have a finite amount of energy in thermal radiation at a single definite frequency. But, on the other hand, there is nothing physically inconsistent in a finite density of radiation energy all of a single frequency. Thermodynamics recognizes two categories of energy : completely disorganized energy, to which statistics applies, and completely organized energy, of which a typical example is the kinetic energy of a single particle. When a system receives energy of the first kind, it is said to receive heat, and when it receives energy of the second kind, it is said to receive mechanical energy (in the generalized sense) or *work*. The distinction between energy received as heat or work is physically significant, and corresponds to experimentally recognizable distinctions. It is evident that if we want to deal with radiation of finite energy and a single definite frequency, we must describe it from the thermodynamic point of view as generalized mechanical energy, and when a system emits radiation of this sort, it must be said to do *work*, not to emit *heat*. Furthermore, since there are no haphazard elements in mechanical energy or work, we are at liberty to submit the machine which does radiational work to any sort of detailed control that we please, so long as this detailed control does not violate the first law of conservation of energy. The second law, dealing only with statistical processes, can impose no restrictions on the control which may be legitimately applied to the radiational machine.

Return now to the consideration of the two metals A and B at 0° Abs with the intermediate space filled with radiation of frequency $\nu_{0B}(\nu_{0B} > \nu_{0A})$. When this radiation impinges on B, it is ineffective as far as photo-electric emission is concerned, since any internal electrons which absorb energy from the radiation do not receive enough to enable them to make their exit, so that they must eventually fall back to their original positions. The electrons of A, on the other hand, may receive from the radiation enough energy to emerge, and in fact all electrons from the upper energy ranges between W_{0A} and $W_{0A} - (h\nu_{0B} - h\nu_{0A})$ may receive enough energy. They emerge with a range of velocities; those coming from the level W_{0A} emerge with kinetic energy $h(\nu_{0B}-\nu_{0A})$, and those from the level $W_{0A} - h(\nu_{0B} - \nu_{0A})$ with 0 kinetic energy. In the space between A and B the emergent electrons are subject to the electric field due to the Volta potential difference. This is in such a direction as to retard the emergent electrons. The fastest electrons travel the greatest distance before stopping, but eventually all the emergent electrons fall back to A, reaching the surface with exactly the same velocity as that with which they emerged, since the electrostatic field is conservative, and are reabsorbed by the metal. This reabsorption is accompanied by the reëmission of radiation. If this radiation were uncontrolled, the reëmitted radiation would contain a range of frequencies, reaching all the way from 0 to $h(\nu_{0B} - \nu_{0A}) + U_A$, so that eventually, by this mechanism, all the original radiation would become diffused through the entire range. There is, however, nothing inconsistent physically in demanding that the reabsorption of electrons be so controlled that reabsorption takes place only when the reradiated energy is of the same frequency as that which originally produced the electron. If this sort of control is applied, both to A and to the reradiation of the internal electrons in B as they drop back from one energy level to another, the system will eventually either settle down into an equilibrium condition in which there is in the intervening space radiation of frequency ν_{0B} and electrons rising from and falling back to A, or else the radiation will gradually disappear, so that finally the energy which was initially in the radiation has gone into the electrons, which circulate in closed cycles across the space from A to B and back to A through the metal.   Now this latter is an impossible situation, if every detail in the process is completely reversible, as it is.   For by reversing the direction of every electron in the final state, which may be done with no expenditure of energy, we would eventually arrive at the initial state, with nothing but radiation between the plates.   The same initial state would therefore at the same time appear as one which had resulted from an initial circulating condition of the electrons, and as one which would automatically degenerate into such a circulating condition.   Hence a contradiction, and we must assume that in the final state there is no net circulation of electrons in the solid metal, but the intervening space between the two metals is filled with two equal streams of electrons in opposite directions.   If this is the necessary final state, then it is easy to see that the electrons which leave A with the maximum velocity are stopped by the Volta potential difference just before they reach the surface of B.   For suppose that they reached the surface of B with a finite velocity, then they would be absorbed by B and complete the cycle through the metal.   If, on the other hand, they did not reach B at all, we could then increase the frequency of the radiation slightly, by an amount still insufficient to bring the electrons across to B.   But now electrons would be emitted by B, which would reach A with velocity increased by the Volta difference, and these electrons would return to B through the metal.   Hence the frequency ν_{0B} just suffices to bring electrons from A across to B against the Volta difference.   This gives

$$h\nu_{0B} + W_{0A} - U_A = eV_{AB}.$$

But by the photo-electric equation,

$$h\nu_{0A} + W_{0A} = U_A.$$

Hence

$$h(\nu_{0B} - \nu_{0A}) = eV_{AB},$$

which is exactly Millikan's equation expressing the independence of the stopping potential of the metal.

I originally gave a theoretical deduction of this equation, using the original Einstein photo-electric equation which assumes that incident light of a single frequency gives rise to emergent electrons of only a single energy. It is especially to be emphasized that the same equation has now been deduced replacing Einstein's relation by the apparently much altered relation which spreads the energy of the emergent electrons over a band. That is, the assumption of a single emergent energy is not pertinent in this connection. One may therefore expect with much plausibility that the same state of affairs will hold for temperatures above 0° Abs, instead of only at 0°, as was assumed in the deduction above, to that degree of approximation to which there is a threshold frequency at higher temperatures.

Experimentally, Millikan found the equality of the stopping potentials to adequately represent the experimental state of affairs for a number of metals, but there were also others for which it failed. He proposed to use the equality of the stopping potentials as a criterion of the " genuineness " of the measured Volta contact potential difference, calling those differences " spurious " which did not satisfy the relation. Thermodynamically, there seems no reason for the existence of " spurious " effects, subject to our assumptions; the existence of such effects must mean the failure of some of the fundamental assumptions. The most important such assumption was that there is no permanent source of energy in the metal, and that we were dealing with a final steady state. If, however, there are surface films which are changing in character there is here a possible source of energy, and it seems very possible that the " spurious " effects are due to the action of such surface films.

In my original thermodynamic discussion of the photo-electric effect I also deduced connections between thermionic emission phenomena and photo-electric phenomena, still assuming the Einstein relation of a sharp photo-electric threshold and a single emergent energy for a single incident frequency. The deduction is no longer valid, but experience with the stopping potentials above would suggest that no great modification would be produced in the final results. The fundamental assumption of the previous discussion certainly continues to hold, namely, that the equilibrium density of the electron vapor in a cavity in a metal at a definite temperature must be the same whether the mechanism which gives rise to the vapor is purely thermionic, or is photoelectric under the black body radiation appropriate to that temperature, or is any mixture of the two. Since the equilibrium distribution of black body radiation is known from thermodynamics, the total photo-electric vapor density could be found if the equilibrium density under light of any single frequency were known. This latter may be found, treating light of any single frequency as a *mechanical* stimulation, and so controlling the details of the reabsorption as to prevent the diffusion of a single frequency into other frequencies. Two principal results were found by the previous analysis. The simplest was that η_0, the latent heat of evaporation of electrons at 0° Abs of formula IV, 33, differs from $h\nu_0$, where ν_0 is the threshold frequency at 0° Abs, by at most a constant, the same for all metals. Experimental results for tungsten make it exceedingly probable that this constant is identically zero. This result, I believe, must stand even with our modified picture of photo-electric emission, although the actual details of the proof would certainly be more complicated and I have not carried them through.

A second relation was that

$$(S_\rho - S_m)_0 + h\left(\frac{d\nu}{d\tau}\right)_0 = \text{univ. Const.,} \qquad \text{VIII, 4.}$$

where $(S_\rho - S_m)_0$ is the difference of entropy at 0° Abs of metal and surface charge which has already appeared in the thermionic emission formula, and $\left(\frac{d\nu}{d\tau}\right)_0$ is the temperature derivative at 0° Abs of the threshold frequency. But now in view of the fact that there is no sharp threshold at temperatures above 0°, this latter relation evidently must be modified. The precise way in which it must be modified is not at present obvious, however, but requires further experimental study of the photo-electric effect. If the new picture of photo-electric emission is correct, then it should be possible to determine U, the barrier potential, from observations of photo-electric emission at frequencies considerably beyond the range of usual measurements. For when $h\nu$ passes the value U, there should be a discontinuity in the slope of the curve giving the number of emitted electrons, as is suggested at once by the distribution curve of Figure 28. U should be an experimentally determinable parameter, therefore. In particular, it may well turn out to be a temperature function, although any temperature dependence has been neglected in theoretical discussions hitherto, and if it is dependent on temperature, its temperature derivative will certainly make a contribution to the term that replaces $\left(\dfrac{d\nu}{d\tau}\right)_0$. It should also be possible to determine the parameter W_0 from the complete photo-electric emission curve. Experimental accuracy is still far from sufficient to permit an answer to the question whether the theoretical curve closely corresponds to the experimental facts, or whether the parameter W_0 which enters the theoretical curve at any temperature is truly the same at all temperatures. Until this question is settled experimentally, there is here the possibility of another contribution to the modified $\left(\dfrac{d\nu}{d\tau}\right)_0$. If the present theory does turn out to be a close approximation, then one may guess that the $U - W_0$ of it will replace the ν_0 of the older theory, the two being equal at $0°$ Abs, and that the temperature derivative of $U - W_0$ will replace $\left(\dfrac{d\nu}{d\tau}\right)_0$ above, and will prove to be simply connected thermodynamically with $(S_\rho - S_m)_0$. This latter is a quantity incapable of direct experimental measurement, but is connected, as we have already seen, with departures of the coefficient of the thermionic emission formula from the universal value. $U - W_0$, on the other hand, and its temperature derivative should eventually be capable of direct measurement. At present the best that can be hoped for is a rough approximation to the temperature derivative of $U - W_0$ obtained by the best adjustment of the experimental data consistent with the Einstein picture of photo-electric emission and the assumption of the existence of a $\dfrac{d\nu_0}{d\tau}$. In this way, numerical values are obtained within the range of variation which experiment seems to demand for the coefficient of the thermionic emission formula. The formula is so constructed that ranges of 10^{14} fold in the coefficient demand apparent fractional temperature coefficients of ν_0 of not more than 3×10^{-4} per degree.

CHAPTER IX

MISCELLANIES

Change of State. Practically all the parameters which we have met in the earlier chapters determinative of the electrical properties of a metal change abruptly when the metal experiences a change of state, either melting from the solid to the liquid, or passing from one modification of the solid to another, and all the formulas in which two different metals appear, usually indicated by the presence of two different subscripts, A and B, may be rewritten for the same metal, denoting by A one modification and by B the other. These parameters for the two states of aggregation usually have to be determined by independent experiment, just as they would for two different metals.

Consider, for example, thermo-electric phenomena. A liquid metal is different thermo-electrically from its solid. This means that the thermo-electric power of a couple composed of one infusible metal and another fusible metal experiences an abrupt discontinuity when the temperature of the upper junction passes through the melting point of the fusible metal. The *total* E.M.F. of such a couple with fixed lower temperature and variable upper temperature is continuous through the melting point, as may be seen by combining equations II, 1 and II, 2. Sometimes in the literature erroneous statements may be found about the nature of the discontinuities. Experimentally, the existence of a discontinuity in thermo-electric power at the melting temperature now seems to be well established [25]; the measurements are not always easy, however, because of the effect of minute impurities in blurring the sharpness of the melting point, and some of the early experimenters failed to find the discontinuity. An expression for the discontinuity in thermo-electric power may be found at once from the fundamental thermo-electric equations, written

177

for solid and liquid at the melting temperature, τ, denoting by A the infusible metal of the thermo-couple. We have:

$$\frac{dE_{A\text{ sol.}}}{d\tau} = \frac{P_{A\text{ sol.}}}{\tau}, \quad \frac{dE_{A\text{ liq.}}}{d\tau} = \frac{P_{A\text{ liq.}}}{\tau}, \qquad \text{IX, 1.}$$

or, for the discontinuity of thermo-electric power,

$$\frac{dE_{A\text{ sol.}}}{d\tau} - \frac{dE_{A\text{ liq.}}}{d\tau} = \frac{P_{A\text{ sol.}} - P_{A\text{ liq.}}}{\tau} = \frac{P_{\text{liq. sol.}}}{\tau}. \qquad \text{IX, 2.}$$

A discontinuity in thermo-electric power hence means a Peltier heat between solid and liquid not identically zero. The discontinuity is evidently independent of the second metal of the couple, and is determined by Peltier heat between solid and liquid.

One would now like to go further and find various relations between the electrical parameters of solid and liquid in terms of some of the ordinary thermodynamic parameters, such, perhaps, as the latent heat of melting. For example, one might be inclined to think that at the melting point the electron vapor in equilibrium with the solid should have the same pressure as the electron vapor in equilibrium with the liquid, in analogy with the fact that the ordinary vapor pressure of liquid and solid are the same at the melting point. Detailed analysis will show, however, that the conventional methods of establishing connections between the ordinary parameters of solid and liquid fail when applied to the electrical parameters. For example, the proof of the equality of ordinary vapor pressure over solid and liquid involves the possibility of entirely converting solid into liquid or liquid into solid by the process of condensation or evaporation through the vapor phase. The same possibility does not exist with regard to the electron vapor, for one cannot by continual evaporation of electrons from the liquid metal make the liquid phase disappear, but there is a residue of negative liquid ions. I have not been successful in devising any method of deducing additional relations between the electrical parameters of different phases by utilizing processes in which one phase is converted into another, but in all such processes in which the pertinent quantities apparently enter, I have found that they persistently cancel from the final result.

I am inclined to think that this is not accidental, that there are no additional necessary relations, and that such quantities as Peltier heat between liquid and solid, Volta potential difference between liquid and solid, latent heat of evaporation of electrons from solid and liquid, and surface heat of charging of solid and liquid, must be determined by independent experiments, except for the relations already given in the earlier chapters which may be specialized for different phases. An attempt which I made to deduce such a relation for the Volta potential difference between solid and liquid was erroneous.[26]

There are, however, other sorts of relation between change of state and electric and magnetic phenomena. A couple of these will be considered here. The first is the effect which a surface charge has on the melting temperature of a metal. A surface charge has an effect on melting temperature analogous to the effect discussed in Chapter V on vapor pressure. It will be instructive to obtain the desired relation by a method different from that used before, and I shall use a method which involves the Volta potential difference be-

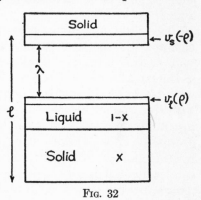

FIG. 32

tween liquid and solid. The fact that this Volta difference cancels from the final result illustrates the remark made above that probably quantities of this sort must be determined by independent experiment.

Construct a Volta condenser, Figure 32, of which one plate consists of solid metal, and the other plate is a layer of liquid overlying a layer of solid, the liquid and solid being in equilibrium. The whole system is at constant temperature. At any temperature the liquid and solid phase may be brought into equilibrium by charging the surface of the plates to the proper charge density. This density may be produced by manipulation of the distance of separation of the plates, since the Volta difference between liquid and solid results in a surface charge which may be varied from 0 to infinity by suitably changing the distance. We suppose that the proper adjustment has been made for equilibrium at every temperature. The relative amount of liquid and solid under equilibrium conditions may be varied by adding or subtracting heat from the system. We suppose the lower plate to contain one gram of metal per unit area, and the fraction x to be solid and $1 - x$ to be liquid. The independent variables will be taken as τ and x. ρ, the surface density, is then a function of temperature only which it is our purpose to evaluate.

There is a mechanical force tending to draw the plates together equal to $2\pi\rho^2$ per unit surface, and this must be equilibrated by the action of a force from without. When ρ is altered by altering the distance between the plates, the system does work through the action of this force. We have then:

$$dW = -Fdl = -2\pi\rho^2\,dl.$$

Call λ the distance from the charge on one plate to that on the other. Then by the condenser relation:

$$4\pi\rho\lambda = V_{ls}, \text{ or } \lambda = \frac{V_{ls}}{4\pi\rho},$$

where V_{ls} is the Volta potential difference between solid and liquid. Further, we have the geometrical relation:

$$l = xv_s + (1 - x)v_l + v_l\,(+\rho) + v_s\,(-\rho) + \lambda,$$

where we have to recognize that surface charges on solid and liquid have different volumes from the metal.

Substitute in this expression for l the value of λ, and form dl in terms of τ and x as independent:

$$dl = (v_s - v_l)dx + \left[x\frac{\partial v_s}{\partial \tau} + (1-x)\frac{\partial v_l}{\partial \tau} + \frac{\partial v_l(+\rho)}{d\tau} + \frac{\partial v_s(-\rho)}{\partial \tau} \right] d\tau$$

$$+ \frac{1}{4\pi}\left[\frac{1}{\rho}\frac{dV_{ls}}{d\tau} - \frac{V_{ls}}{\rho^2}\frac{d\rho}{d\tau} \right] d\tau.$$

Write the first law,

$$dQ = dE + dW = \frac{\partial E}{\partial \tau} d\tau + \frac{\partial E}{\partial x} dx + dW,$$

and substitute for dl, getting:

$$dQ = \left\{ \frac{\partial E}{\partial \tau} - 2\pi\rho^2 \left[x \frac{\partial v_s}{\partial \tau} + (1-x) \frac{\partial v_l}{\partial \tau} + \frac{\partial v_l(+\rho)}{\partial \tau} + \frac{\partial v_s(-\rho)}{\partial \tau} \right] \right.$$
$$\left. - \frac{\rho^2}{2} \left[\frac{1}{\rho} \frac{\partial V_{ls}}{\partial \tau} - \frac{V_{ls}}{\rho^2} \frac{d\rho}{d\tau} \right] \right\} d\tau + \left\{ \frac{\partial E}{\partial x} - 2\pi\rho^2 (v_s - v_l) \right\} dx.$$

Now form the differential of entropy, dS, by dividing by τ, and express the condition that dS is a perfect differential. Only the terms in the coefficient of $d\tau$ which are a function of x enter this relation. It is seen at once that none of the terms involving the Volta potential difference involve x, so that V_{ls} drops out of the final result. The same is true of the terms involving the volume of the surface charge. The condition on the coefficients now becomes, after simple reduction:

$$\left(\frac{\partial Q}{\partial x} \right)_\tau = - 4\pi\rho \frac{d\rho}{d\tau} \tau(v_s - v_l).$$

$\left(\frac{\partial Q}{\partial x} \right)_\tau$ is obviously the negative of the ordinary latent heat of melting, L, so that the relation may be written:

$$\frac{1}{4\pi\rho} \frac{d\tau}{d\rho} = - \frac{\tau(v_l - v_s)}{L}, \qquad \text{IX, 3.}$$

giving the desired dependence of melting temperature on surface charge.

The effect of surface charge on melting found in this way proves to be due entirely to the internal pressure accompanying the surface charge. This is what might be expected, because the surface charge is accompanied by no electric field in the interior of the metal, so that the only possible effect of the surface charge at the surface of contact of liquid and solid is the pressure arising from the charge. The internal pressure produced by the charge is $p = -2\pi\rho^2$. Hence $dp = -4\pi\rho\,d\rho$, which, substituted in equation 3, reduces it at once to the familiar Clapeyron's equation.

The second example is the effect of a magnetic field on the melting point of any substance, metallic or not. A precisely similar problem would be to find the effect of an electric field on the melting temperature of a dielectric. It is, of course, well known that there is an exact formal parallelism between phenomena in dielectrics and those in materials with magnetic permeability, the formulas applicable to a dielectric being at once applicable to the magnetic material on replacing ϵ, $\mathcal{E}$, and D (dielectric constant, electric field, and electric displacement) by μ, H, and B (magnetic permeability, magnetic field, and magnetic induction). It will be sufficient, therefore, to deduce the formulas

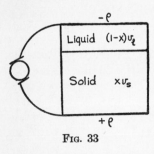

FIG. 33

for one case only, and we choose the dielectric, since the corresponding physical manipulations are a little easier to visualize. Given, then, a condenser, between the plates of which there is one gram of dielectric per unit area (Figure 33). The dielectric is partly solid and partly liquid, the fraction x being in the solid phase. The coatings of the condenser are rigidly attached to the dielectric, so that their distance apart changes in response to the changes of dimensions accompanying melting. The plates may be charged to any desired potential and therefore to any desired charge density by a suitable electric machine in the circuit connecting the coatings. This charge density is to be maintained at any temperature at just that value which is necessary to produce equilibrium between liquid and solid at that temperature, so that ρ is a function of temperature only. The independent variables fixing the condition of the system are chosen as τ and x. The system does work against the electric engine when charge passes from one plate to the other of amount

$$dW = -V\,d\rho = -V\frac{d\rho}{d\tau}\,d\tau.$$

The potential difference, in terms of charge, dielectric constants, and dimensions, is :

$$V = \frac{4\pi\rho}{\epsilon_s} xv_s + \frac{4\pi\rho}{\epsilon_l} (1 - x) v_l,$$

where ϵ_s and ϵ_l are the dielectric constants of solid and liquid. Substitution of these values into the expression of the first law, $dQ = dE + dW$, now gives :

$$dQ = \left\{ \frac{\partial E}{\partial \tau} - 4\pi\rho \frac{d\rho}{d\tau} \left[x \frac{v_s}{\epsilon_s} + (1 - x) \frac{v_l}{\epsilon_l} \right] \right\} d\tau + \frac{\partial E}{\partial x} dx.$$

Divide by τ to form dS, and express the condition that dS is a perfect differential, obtaining at once

$$\left(\frac{\partial Q}{\partial x} \right)_\tau \equiv - L = \tau 4\pi\rho \frac{d\rho}{d\tau} \left(\frac{v_s}{\epsilon_s} - \frac{v_l}{\epsilon_l} \right). \qquad \text{IX, 4.}$$

This may be expressed in terms of the electric force within the dielectric, or better in terms of the dielectric displacement, D, which is continuous in solid and liquid. $D = 4\pi\rho$, $dD = 4\pi d\rho$.

$$L = - \tau \frac{D}{4\pi} \frac{dD}{d\tau} \left(\frac{v_s}{\epsilon_s} - \frac{v_l}{\epsilon_l} \right), \qquad \text{IX, 5.}$$

an expression giving the effect of dielectric displacement on melting temperature, *with this particular set-up*.

This effect on melting temperature is entirely accounted for in terms of the internal stress accompanying the dielectric displacement. The internal pressure may be found in terms of the discontinuity in the Maxwell stress $\left(\frac{\epsilon}{8\pi} \mathcal{E}^2 \right)$ on passing into the dielectric. In the solid phase there is a discontinuity on passing the coating of the condenser of $\frac{\epsilon_s}{8\pi} \mathcal{E}_s^2 = \frac{1}{8\pi} \frac{D^2}{\epsilon_s}$, and since there is no Maxwell stress at all in the space outside the condenser, this is the total internal stress in the solid in virtue of electrostriction. In the same way the total stress in the liquid is $\frac{1}{8\pi} \frac{D^2}{\epsilon_l}$. There is thus a discontinuity in internal pressure on crossing from solid to liquid, the discontinuity being equilibrated by the electric action in the surface of transition. Formula 5 may now at once be written :

$$d\tau = - \frac{\tau}{L} [v_s \, dp_s - v_l \, dp_l], \qquad \text{IX, 6.}$$

and this is at once recognized as the familiar generalization of Clapeyron's to the case where unequal increments of pressure act on solid and liquid. There is therefore no specific effect of the electric field inside the dielectric on the melting point, but the entire effect is an electrostriction effect. This conclusion might at first appear surprising, but it is consistent with the result just found for a metal. It is not easy to pass directly, by specialization of constants, from the formula for the metal to that for the dielectric, because for one thing the internal stress in the metal with surface charge is a *tension*, while that in the dielectric is a *pressure*.

It is particularly to be emphasized that formula 5 above, as an explicit formula for the effect of dielectric displacement on melting point, is good only when the electric field is applied in such a way that the internal pressure arising from electrostriction is the same as above. This is not always the case, or in other words the internal pressure is not a unique function of dielectric displacement, so that the internal condition of the dielectric is not uniquely determined by its prevailing displacement, even when the surfaces are free from mechanical stress applied as an independent variable. This may at once seem to be the case by considering a condenser in which the plates are held rigidly fixed at a definite distance apart and a slab of dielectric is inserted between them, the rest of the space between the plates being dielectrically neutral. In this case the internal pressure in the solid is $\dfrac{D^2}{8\pi} \left[\dfrac{1}{\epsilon_s} - 1 \right]$ and that in the liquid $\dfrac{D^2}{8\pi} \left[\dfrac{1}{\epsilon_l} - 1 \right]$, which are thus of opposite signs from the case above. A correspondingly different formula will be found for the connection between dielectric displacement and melting temperature in this case, but when expressed in terms of internal pressure, it again reduces to the generalized Clapeyron's equation.

That the electrostriction effects are different, depending on the method of applying the field, has been shown by explicit experiment.[27]

Exactly similar expressions hold for the connection between magnetic induction and the melting temperature (or transition temperature between two phases). The formal analysis for the magnetic case must involve a somewhat different physical set-up from the electrical case, because magnetic condensers, with arbitrarily variable magnetic charge density, do not exist. A corresponding set-up for the magnetic case would be to construct the core of a solenoid out of the magnetic material, and take work out of the system through the E.M.F. generated inductively when the magnetic permeability, and so the flux through the windings of the solenoid, changes, neglecting Joulean dissipation, or assuming the windings of the solenoid to be made of supraconducting material.

These formulas have not made explicit use of the fact that the molecular structure passes through a discontinuity, that is, they have not assumed a polymorphic transition in the ordinary sense. They apply, therefore, to the displacement by an electric field of the temperature of discontinuity, whether that discontinuity is a discontinuity in volume only, dielectric constant only, or heat content (latent heat) only, or any combination of them. In particular, formula 5 shows that if there is no discontinuity in volume but a discontinuity in dielectric constant, then the temperature of discontinuity is displaced by a finite amount by a change of field if there is also a finite latent heat to mark the temperature of discontinuity of dielectric constant, but if the latent heat vanishes, then the temperature of discontinuity is displaced by an infinite amount. Hence in general, a discontinuity in dielectric constant is accompanied by a latent heat, whether or not there is an accompanying discontinuity of volume, or else the temperature of discontinuity as measured in an ordinary experiment will exhibit apparent instabilities. The same remarks obviously apply to discontinuities in magnetic permeability.

Miscellaneous Effects of Temperature and Pressure. For possible convenience of reference, and because they have an intrinsic interest, various simple relations are collected here.

(*a*) There is a connection between the temperature coefficient of dielectric constant (or magnetic permeability) and a heating effect when the electric (or magnetic) field in the medium is changed isothermally.

To find this relation a set-up may be used very similar to that already used for finding the effect of surface charge on melting point. Construct a condenser with unit mass of the dielectric standing on unit area, the plates resting on the dielectric and following any change of dimensions. Charge the plates to arbitrary charge density by a suitable electric machine. Take as independent variables temperature, τ, and charge density, ρ. Then $dW = -V d\rho = -\dfrac{4\pi\rho}{\epsilon} v \, d\rho$, where v is the specific volume of the dielectric and ϵ its dielectric constant. Then:

$$dQ = \frac{\partial E}{\partial \tau} d\tau + \left(\frac{\partial E}{\partial \rho} - \frac{4\pi\rho}{\epsilon} v \right) d\rho.$$

The condition that $dS, = \dfrac{dQ}{\tau}$, is a perfect differential is:

$$\frac{1}{\tau}\left(\frac{\partial Q}{\partial \rho}\right)_\tau = 4\pi\rho \left[\frac{v}{\epsilon^2}\frac{\partial \epsilon}{\partial \tau} - \frac{1}{\epsilon}\frac{\partial v}{\partial \tau} \right), \qquad \text{IX, 7.}$$

which gives the heating effect on charging the dielectric under these particular conditions. We may suspect that at least part of this heating effect arises from the change of internal pressure accompanying the application of the field. The ordinary formula for the heating effect accompanying a change of pressure is $\left(\dfrac{\partial Q}{\partial p}\right)_\tau = -\tau\left(\dfrac{\partial v}{\partial \tau}\right)_p$. In this case the internal pressure arising from electrostriction is $p = \dfrac{2\pi\rho^2}{\epsilon}$, and $dp = \dfrac{4\pi\rho \, d\rho}{\epsilon}$, giving

$$\left\{ \frac{1}{\tau}\left(\frac{\partial Q}{\partial \rho}\right)_\tau \right\}_{\text{electrostriction}} = -4\pi\rho\,\frac{1}{\epsilon}\frac{\partial v}{\partial \tau}.$$

But this is exactly the second term in formula 7. The first term therefore represents a specific heating effect of the internal field, so that there is here a specific effect of the field, unlike the situation with respect to melting. The formula may now be written :

$$\left\{\left(\frac{\partial Q}{\partial D}\right)_\tau\right\}_{\text{specific}} = \tau\,\frac{D}{4\,\pi}\,\frac{v}{\epsilon^2}\,\frac{d\epsilon}{d\tau}. \qquad\qquad \text{IX, 8.}$$

To find the total heating effect with any particular physical set-up the heating due to the electrostriction must be added to this term.

A precisely similar formula, of course, holds for the magnetic case :

$$\left\{\left(\frac{\partial Q}{\partial B}\right)_\tau\right\}_{\text{specific}} = \tau\,\frac{B}{4\,\pi}\,\frac{v}{\mu^2}\,\frac{d\mu}{d\tau}. \qquad\qquad \text{IX, 9.}$$

(b) The effect of hydrostatic pressure on dielectric constant (or magnetic permeability) may be connected with other parameters by an extension of the argument above. Use the same condenser as before, but now allow a hydrostatic pressure to act, so that the work becomes $dW = -\,V\,d\rho + p\,dl$. Take as independent variables τ, ρ, and p. Then,

$$dQ = \left(\frac{\partial E}{\partial \tau} + p\,\frac{\partial l}{\partial \tau}\right)d\tau + \left(\frac{\partial E}{\partial \rho} + p\,\frac{\partial l}{\partial \rho} - \frac{4\,\pi\rho}{\epsilon}\,l\right)d\rho + \left(\frac{\partial E}{\partial p} + p\,\frac{\partial l}{\partial p}\right)dp.$$

At constant temperature dQ is a perfect differential, so we have at once the condition that the cross derivatives of the coefficients of $d\rho$ and dp must be equal. This gives, replacing l by v, which may be done since the dielectric is supposed fluid so that unit mass always stands on unit area,

$$\frac{\partial v}{\partial \rho} = 4\,\pi\rho\left[\frac{1}{\epsilon}\,\frac{\partial v}{\partial p} - \frac{v}{\epsilon^2}\,\frac{\partial \epsilon}{\partial p}\right],$$

or

$$\frac{\partial v}{\partial D} = \frac{D}{4\,\pi}\left[\frac{1}{\epsilon}\,\frac{\partial v}{\partial p} - \frac{v}{\epsilon^2}\,\frac{\partial \epsilon}{\partial p}\right].$$

Hence the volume of a dielectric changes when it experiences an electric field, and this change is connected with the pressure coefficient of dielectric constant. Part of this change of volume is evidently connected with the change of internal pressure accompanying the change of D. Since the electrostriction internal pressure is $\dfrac{D^2}{8\,\pi\epsilon}$, $dp_{\text{electrostriction}} = \dfrac{D\,dD}{4\,\pi\epsilon}$, and it is at once evident that the first term in the formula just derived is the electrostriction change of volume. The remaining term represents the specific change of volume with applied field, arising from something like an orientation of the dipoles, and is :

$$\left[\left(\frac{\partial v}{\partial D}\right)_{\tau,\,p}\right]_{\text{specific}} = -\,\frac{D}{4\,\pi}\,\frac{v}{\epsilon^2}\,\frac{\partial\epsilon}{\partial p}. \qquad \text{IX, 10.}$$

It is well established by experiment that $\dfrac{\partial\epsilon}{\partial p} \neq 0$, so that the change of volume due to polarization or realignment of the dipoles is a real effect. The total change of volume when field is applied must be obtained by adding to this the electrostriction term, which will depend on the particular set-up.

A precisely similar formula holds for the magnetic case :

$$\left[\left(\frac{\partial v}{\partial B}\right)_{\tau,\,p}\right]_{\text{specific}} = -\,\frac{B}{4\,\pi}\,\frac{v}{\mu^2}\,\frac{\partial\mu}{\partial p}. \qquad \text{IX, 11.}$$

In the analysis above any net change of volume when the plates of the condenser are charged is neglected, which amounts to assuming that the volume is increased as much by the positive surface charge as it is diminished by the negative charge. This assumption is justified as long as the effects are linear in the charge ; if there are non-linear effects, they must vanish at small charge densities, and the above is a valid first approximation.

(c) The Effect of Pressure on Volta Potential Difference. The desired effect might be found by a simple generalization of the analysis of Chapter III, allowing a hydrostatic pressure to act on the system in addition to the other forces, and supplementing the expression for dW by the additional term $p\,dv$. This was the method adopted in my Physical Review paper of 1919. The analysis may be simplified, however, by omitting the external battery by which the condenser plates are charged to any arbitrary charge density, and taking mechanical work out of the system merely by allowing the distance between the plates to change against the mechanical force tending to draw the plates together. No external work is done by the passage of current in the wire connecting the plates, because the system is now by hypothesis always in electrical equilibrium, and the effective potential acting against transfer of charge is zero, by I, 7 bis. The condenser plates shall further contain unit mass of metal standing on unit area, which amounts to assuming that the metal is liquid, or that the only stress to which they are subjected is a hydrostatic pressure. We now have to recognize explicitly the volume occupied by the surface charges, because, even considering only linear terms, one would not expect in general the volume of a surface charge on the metal A to be the same as on B. The conventional method of attack is now employed. As independent variables choose τ, p, and ρ. First write dW,

$$dW = - F\,dl + p\,dv = -2\,\pi\rho^2\,dl + p\,dv.$$

Here v is the total volume of the material parts of the system, including neutral metals A and B and their surface charges.

$$l = v + \lambda, \text{ and } 4\,\pi\rho\lambda = V_{BA},$$

or
$$l = v + \frac{V_{BA}}{4\,\pi\rho}.$$

Expressing the differentials in terms of the independent variables,

$$dl = dv + \frac{1}{4\,\pi}\left[\frac{1}{\rho}\left(\frac{\partial V}{\partial \tau}\,d\tau + \frac{\partial V}{\partial p}\,dp + \frac{\partial V}{\partial \rho}\,d\rho\right) - \frac{V}{\rho^2}\,d\rho\right].$$

$$dv = \frac{\partial v}{\partial \tau}\,d\tau + \frac{\partial v}{\partial p}\,dp + \frac{\partial v}{\partial \rho}\,d\rho.$$

Putting now $dQ = dE + dW$, and forming $dS = dQ/\tau$, we find :
(1) the coefficient of $d\tau$ is :

$$\frac{1}{\tau}\left[\frac{\partial E}{\partial \tau} + p\,\frac{\partial v}{\partial \tau} - 2\,\pi\rho^2\left(\frac{\partial v}{\partial \tau} + \frac{1}{4\,\pi\rho}\,\frac{\partial V_{BA}}{\partial \tau}\right)\right],$$

(2) the coefficient of dp is :

$$\frac{1}{\tau}\left[\frac{\partial E}{\partial p} + p\,\frac{\partial v}{\partial p} - 2\,\pi\rho^2\left(\frac{\partial v}{\partial p} + \frac{1}{4\,\pi\rho}\,\frac{\partial V_{BA}}{\partial p}\right)\right],$$

(3) the coefficient of $d\rho$ is :

$$\frac{1}{\tau}\left[\frac{\partial E}{\partial \rho} + p\,\frac{\partial v}{\partial \rho} - 2\,\pi\rho^2\left(\frac{\partial v}{\partial \rho} + \frac{1}{4\,\pi\rho}\,\frac{\partial V_{BA}}{\partial \rho} - \frac{V_{BA}}{4\,\pi\rho^2}\right)\right].$$

The cross derivatives of the coefficients of dp and $d\rho$ give the information of immediate interest here. This condition reduces to :

$$\frac{\partial V_{BA}}{\partial p} = -\frac{\partial v}{\partial \rho} - 4\,\pi\rho\,\frac{\partial v}{\partial p}. \qquad\text{IX, 12.}$$

The first term on the right-hand side, $\dfrac{\partial v}{\partial \rho}$, contains two effects.

There is in the first place an electrostriction effect on the volume of the metals themselves; there can be no other internal effect in the metals, because the electrostriction change of internal pressure is the only internal effect of the surface charge, the electric field inside the metal always vanishing. In the second place, there is an effect arising from the actual volume of the charge on the surface; if this volume is different on A than on B, then there is a change of net volume when charge passes from A to B. The first term arising from electrostriction can be found at once. The internal pressure, Π, of electrostriction origin, is $-2\,\pi\rho^2$. Hence $d\Pi = -4\,\pi\rho\,d\rho$. The corresponding change of volume $= \dfrac{\partial v}{\partial p}\,d\Pi = -4\,\pi\rho\,\dfrac{\partial v}{\partial p}\,d\rho$. But this cancels the second term on the right-hand side, so that the formula reduces to :

$$\frac{\partial V_{BA}}{\partial p} = \begin{array}{l}\text{(vol. of unit surface charge on } A) \\ -\ \text{(vol. of unit surface charge on } B).\end{array} \qquad\text{IX, 13.}$$

If, therefore, the effect of pressure on the Volta potential difference could be measured, we would get some hold on the volume of the surface charge. There seems no way of direct experimental attack on this question, because up to the present no medium sufficiently neutral in character is known to permit the application of pressure without at the same time introducing surface complications that would vitiate any measurement of the Volta difference. However, V_{BA} sometimes enters into other relations in which the effect of pressure may be directly measured on some of the terms, as for example, relations in which the Peltier heat is involved, so that the formula just obtained may be of value indirectly in other situations.

If the hydrostatic pressure acts on only one of the metals, then only one of the surface charges appears in the formula. In particular, the Volta difference between normal metal and the same metal compressed by unit pressure is equal to the volume of the surface charge on the metal.

(*d*) With regard to the general effects of hydrostatic pressure the remarks already made about change of state apply. A metal free from stress and the same metal subjected to pressure may be regarded as two different metals; all the formulas already written in which two metals *A* and *B* appear apply at once, and yield relations between the pressure coefficients and various other parameters. In particular, a thermo-couple may be constructed of which one branch is a normal metal and the other the same metal exposed to pressure. There is a Peltier heat when electricity passes from compressed to uncompressed metal, and the Thomson heat of the compressed metal is different from that of the uncompressed metal. These Peltier and Thomson heats are connected with the total E.M.F. of the " pressure thermo-couple " in the same way as the Peltier and Thomson heats of an ordinary couple composed of two different metals. These effects are not difficult to measure experimentally, and I have made such measurements for a number of metals [28]; the variations with pressure and temperature are often quite complicated.

(*e*) The effect of pressure on the Hall coefficient may be found by an extension of the argument used in Chapter VII. We use exactly the same set-up as considered there, a persistent current flowing in a metal with a perpendicular magnetic field, but in addition we allow a hydrostatic pressure to act in the system. The work done by the system becomes

$$dW = \frac{RIH}{d} \, dq_e + p \, dv.$$

Choose as independent variables τ, q_e, and p. Then

$$\frac{dQ}{\tau} = \frac{1}{\tau}\left\{\left[\frac{\partial E}{\partial \tau} + p\,\frac{\partial v}{\partial \tau}\right]d\tau + \left[\frac{\partial E}{\partial q_e} + p\,\frac{\partial v}{\partial q_e} + \frac{RIH}{d}\right]dq_e\right.$$
$$\left. + \left[\frac{\partial E}{\partial p} + p\,\frac{\partial v}{\partial p}\right]dp\right\}.$$

Equating the cross derivatives of the coefficients of $d\tau$ and dq_e, and of $d\tau$ and dp gives no new information. The condition on the coefficients of dq_e and dp gives :

$$H\frac{\partial}{\partial p}\left(\frac{RI}{d}\right) = -\frac{\partial v}{\partial q_e}. \qquad \text{IX, 14.}$$

There will evidently be a pressure effect on the total current arising from the compressibility of the material of the circuit, and the resulting change of self-induction when pressure changes. Neglecting this compressibility effect,

$$H\frac{\partial}{\partial p}\,(Ri) = -\frac{\partial v}{\partial q_e}, \qquad \text{IX, 15.}$$

where now the formula applies to a plate of unit cross section. Since the primary current changes when the energy of the system is tapped by drawing transverse current, the term $\dfrac{\partial v}{\partial q_e}$ refers to a change of volume of a conductor when the current in it changes. There will be such a change of volume from electrostriction and magnetostriction effects in any event. But it may well be that there is a specific effect of current on volume, independent of any stress effects. Such effects must be exceedingly minute, and as far as I know no attempt has been made to find them. They would differ from electrostriction effects in being linear in the current. The left-hand side of equation 15 is exactly analogous to the left-hand side of VII, 11. The pressure derivative of R may be determined by direct experiment, although as far as I am aware no actual attempt has been made to measure this deriva-tive. There is also on the left-hand side the term $\dfrac{\partial i}{\partial p}$; analogy with the previous analysis would lead one to suspect that in general this will not vanish. It almost certainly will not vanish if the volume of the conductor is a function of current. We must, therefore, in general recognize the possibility of a pressure E.M.F. in a circuit in which the hydrostatic pressure is changing, like the E.M.F. arising from change of temperature already considered in Chapter VII. This pressure E.M.F. must be linear in the total current and involve the pressure coefficient of the Hall coefficient. Whether or not the term $\dfrac{\partial v}{\partial q_e}$ is negligible, we would have an expression for the E.M.F. when pressure is changing of the form i (press. e.m.f.) $\dfrac{dp}{dt}$, where (press. e.m.f.) is the value of this E.M.F. for unit current and unit rate of change of pressure, and is a function only of the construction of the circuit.

We may make an analysis exactly like that on page 141, now allowing pressure to act on the circuit carrying the persistent current, and tapping energy out of the system by an E.M.F., ϵ. The previous analysis carries through, with the addition of a $p\,dv$ term in the work, and an additional term, i (press. e.m.f.) $\dfrac{dp}{dt}$, in the E.M.F. We have then, taking τ, i, and p as variables,

$$\frac{dQ}{\tau} = \frac{1}{\tau}\left\{\left[\frac{\partial E}{\partial \tau} + p\,\frac{\partial v}{\partial \tau} + i^2\,(\text{temp. e.m.f.})\right]d\tau\right.$$

$$+ \left[\frac{\partial E}{\partial i} + p\,\frac{\partial v}{\partial i} + iL\right]di + \left.\left[\frac{\partial E}{\partial p} + p\,\frac{\partial v}{\partial p} + i^2\,(\text{press. e.m.f.})\right]dp\right\}.$$

The condition on the coefficients of $d\tau$ and di is :

$$\frac{\partial Q}{\partial i} = \tau\left[i\,\frac{\partial L}{\partial \tau} - 2\,i\,(\text{temp. e.m.f.})\right] \qquad \text{IX, 16.}$$

as before, where now the thermal expansion of the circuit is not neglected.

The condition on the coefficients of di and dp is :

$$2\,i\,(\text{press. e.m.f.}) = i\,\frac{\partial L}{\partial p} + \frac{\partial v}{\partial i}. \qquad \text{IX, 17.}$$

The first term on the right-hand side represents that part of the pressure E.M.F. arising from the change of self-induction due to the compression of the material by the applied hydrostatic pressure. The second term, $\frac{dv}{di}$, after the electrostriction terms have been subtracted, may be said to give the specific pressure E.M.F.

The condition on the coefficients of $d\tau$ and dp gives, after cancelling $\frac{\partial Q}{\partial p}$ and $-\tau \frac{\partial v}{\partial \tau}$, which are equal by a well-known result of elementary thermodynamics :

$$\frac{\partial}{\partial p} \text{ (temp. e.m.f.)} = \frac{\partial}{\partial \tau} \text{ (press. e.m.f.).} \qquad \text{IX, 18.}$$

These various quantities are at present very far beyond experimental reach.

This discussion of miscellanies might be continued indefinitely ; every sort of an external disturbance changes in general all the physical parameters of a substance, and in many cases these changes are interrelated thermodynamically. Thus if the body is solid, stresses may be applied instead of a simple hydrostatic pressure, and the effect of any particular kind of stress may be found by simple extensions of the methods used for hydrostatic pressure. The situation becomes enormously complicated if effects are considered in single crystals. It is usually obvious enough what sort of relations may be expected to be given by thermodynamics, but there are some cases where it is more difficult to see just what are the limitations of the thermodynamic method of attack. Thus one might perhaps expect relations in addition to those mentioned above for the effect of pressure on the thermo-electric parameters, obtainable by some combination of pressure with a cycle in which there are irreversible effects, discarding the irreversible effects by an argument similar to that advanced in Chapter II to justify the deduction of the Kelvin relations for an ordinary thermo-electric circuit. I have not been able to find any such method, however, and it is not now clear to me whether such relations might be worked out or not.

In any event, it would be futile to attempt to anticipate all possible needs, and the list given here must suffice. Other relations may be deduced as the need for them arises by methods similar to those used here.

REFERENCES

List of papers of P. W. Bridgman, the substance of which is collected into this book:

A Critical Thermodynamic Discussion of the Volta, Thermo-Electric and Thermionic Effects. Phys. Rev. 14, 306–347, 1919.

The Connections between the Four Transverse Galvanomagnetic and Thermomagnetic Phenomena. Phys. Rev. 644–651, 1924.

The Universal Constant of Thermionic Emission. Phys. Rev. 27, 173–180, 1926.

The Transverse Thermo-Electric Effect in Metal Crystals. Proc. Nat. Acad. Sci. 13, 46–50, 1927.

Electrical Properties of Single Metal Crystals. Report of the Volta Congress at Como, 10 pp., 1927.

General Considerations on the Photo-Electric Effect. Phys. Rev. 31, 90–100, 1928.

Note on the Principle of Detailed Balancing. Phys. Rev. 31, 101–102, 1927.

Thermoelectric Phenomena in Crystals and General Electrical Concepts. Phys. Rev. 31, 221–235, 1928.

The Photoelectric Effect and Thermionic Emission: A Correction and an Extension. Phys. Rev. 31, 862–866, 1928.

Resistance and Thermoelectric Phenomena in Metal Crystals. Proc. Nat. Acad. Sci. 14, 943–946, 1928.

Thermoelectric Phenomena and Electrical Resistance in Single Metal Crystals. Proc. Amer. Acad. 63, 351–399, 1929.

On the Application of Thermodynamics to the Thermoelectric Circuit. Proc. Nat. Acad. Sci. 15, 765–768, 1929.

On the Nature of the Transverse Thermomagnetic Effect and the Transverse Thermoelectric Effect in Crystals. Proc. Nat. Acad. Sci. 15, 768–773, 1929.

General Considerations on the Emission of Electrons from Conductors under Intense Fields. Phys. Rev. 34, 1411–1417, 1929.

New Kinds of E.M.F. and Other Effects Thermodynamically Connected with the Four Transverse Effects. Phys. Rev. 39, 702–715, 1932.

Comments on the Note by E. H. Kennard on "Entropy, Reversible Processes and Thermo-Couples." Proc. Nat. Acad. Sci. 18, 242–245, 1932.

REFERENCES IN THE BODY OF THE TEXT

1. C. Benedicks. A summary, with references to other papers, will be found in an article by Benedicks in Ergebnisse der Exakten Natur-Wissenschaften, Vol. VIII, 1929, entitled: Jetziger Stand der grundlegenden Kenntnisse der Thermoelektrizität. During the reading of the proofs of this book a paper has appeared by C. Benedicks and C. Siljeholm, Arkiv för Matematik, Astronomi och Fysik, 24A, No. 7, 1933, in which new experiments and arguments are given for the reality of the Benedicks effect in homogeneous metals.
2. For example, G. Borelius, Ann. der Phys. 56, 394, 1918.
3. L. Boltzmann, Ber. Wien. Akad. 96, II, 1258, 1887.
4. E. H. Kennard, Proc. Nat. Acad. Sci. 18, 237–241, 1932.
   P. W. Bridgman, Proc. Nat. Acad. Sci. 18, 242–245, 1932.
5. H. A. Lorentz, Wied. Ann. 36, 593, 1889.
   Lord Kelvin, Proc. Roy. Soc. Edin. 22, 118, 1897–99.
6. L. Tonks and I. Langmuir, Phys. Rev. 29, 524–531, 1927.
7. M. von Laue, Jahrb. d. Rad. u. Elek. 15, 257–270, 1918.
8. See, for example, a summarizing article by L. Nordheim, Phys. ZS. 30, 177, 1929.
9. P. W. Bridgman, Phys. Rev. 34, 1411–1417, 1929.
10. P. Ehrenfest und A. J. Rutgers, Proc. Amst. Acad. 32, 698–706; 883–893, 1929.
11. W. Thomson, Proc. Roy. Soc. Edin. 3, 255, 1854.
    Trans. Roy. Soc. Edin. 21, 153, 1857 (Principal reference)
    Phil. Mag. 11, 379, 1856.
    Math. and Phys. Papers, 1, 232, 287, 1882.
12. G. Borelius und A. E. Lindh, Ann. d. Phys. 53, 97–137, 1917.
13. P. W. Bridgman, Proc. Nat. Acad. Sci. 13, 46–50, 1927.
14. T. Terada and T. Tsutsui, Proc. Imp. Acad. Tok. 3, 132–135, 1927.
15. P. W. Bridgman, Proc. Amer. Acad. 63, 351–399, 1929.
16. H. P. Stabler, Phys. Rev. 37, 461, 1931.
    E. A. Uehling, Phys. Rev. 39, 821–830, 1932.
17. H. A. Lorentz, Report of the Fourth Solvay Congress, "Conductibilité Électrique des Métaux," 354–360.
18. P. W. Bridgman, Collection of Thermodynamic Formulas, Harvard University Press, 1925.
19. J. Frenkel, Wave Mechanics, Elementary Theory, Oxford, Clarendon Press, 1932.
20. L. Nordheim, Phys. ZS. 30, 177–196, 1929.
21. J. Frenkel, Phil. Mag. 33, 297–321, 1917.
22. R. H. Fowler, Phys. Rev. 38, 45–56, 1931.
23. See papers in the Physical Review for 1928 given above.
24. R. A. Millikan, Phys. Rev. 7, 18, 355, 1916.
25. See, for example, T. R. Harrison and P. D. Foote, Jour. Opt. Soc. Amer. 7, 389, 1923.
26. P. W. Bridgman, Phys. Rev. 14, 346, 1919.
27. See discussion of the experimental material in a theoretical paper by E. C. Kemble, Phys. Rev. 7, 614–624, 1916.
28. P. W. Bridgman, Proc. Amer. Acad. 53, 269–386, 1918.

INDEX